Lessons with Master Liang

**T'ai-Chi,
Philosophy,
and Life**

Lessons With Master Liang

T'ai-Chi, Philosophy, and Life

Compiled and Edited by Ray Hayward

Revised and Expanded 3rd Edition

Ray Hayward Enterprises, LLC

Lessons With Master Liang:
T'ai-Chi, Philosophy, and Life

Originally titled *T'ai-Chi Ch'uan: Lessons with Master T.T. Liang*

First Printing – 1993.
Revised, expanded edition – 2000.
Re-revision, expanded further – 2010.

Photographs courtesy of T.T. Liang, An-le Liang, Joseph Liang, Dan Polsfuss, Paul Gallagher, Jonathan Russel, Mike Cain, Paul Abdella, and the author.

Published by: **Ray Hayward Enterprises, LLC**

Disclaimer: The author and publisher of this book are not responsible for any injury that may result from following the instructions contained herein. The reader should consult his or her physician for advice before attempting any such activities.

ISBN 978-0-692-07084-0
3 4 5 6 7 8 / 23 22 21 20 19 18

Table of Contents

Foreword

By Paul Abdella

In the spring of 1982, I began studying T'ai-Chi Ch'uan with Master T.T. Liang. I joined a small group of students who met weekly in the basement of his home in St. Cloud, Minnesota. Master Liang had recently moved to St. Cloud after having spent a dozen or so years living and teaching in Boston. He moved to St. Cloud to "retire" from teaching, but news of his arrival preceded him and soon he had a steady stream of hopeful students seeking out his instruction.

A typical class with Master Liang was anything but typical. Of course, there was always instruction in the forms and techniques of T'ai-Chi plus wonderful stories of the Old Master. However, it was Master Liang's playful intimidations and disarming sense of humor, aimed squarely at a student's hidden vulnerabilities, that made class with Liang an opportunity to learn something about oneself.

Paul Abdella, right, with Master T.T. Liang and Ray Hayward at Liang's residence in New Jersey, circa 1999.

As I was reading through this book, I was instantly transported back to the crowded little basement in St. Cloud where I watched and listened to Master Liang describe his views on T'ai-Chi and life.

My friend Ray Hayward has, with great care and patience, compiled accurate transcriptions of his classes with Master Liang spanning a period of more than a dozen years. He has presented an honest portrait of a man who has dedicated himself to the experience, preservation and transmission of T'ai-Chi as a living tradition accessible to all who seek out its subtleties and inner beauty. In the process, Ray has revealed much about himself. As someone who seeks truth and meaning in life, T'ai-Chi for Ray has always been a path of transformation and personal growth.

To the reader of this book: Master Liang's approach to T'ai-Chi was always simple— to learn all you can from teachers and books, to practice daily and most of all, to enjoy life. If this book can assist you on your journey, as it has for me, I'm glad. May you take these "Lessons with Master Liang" and savor the gift that is T'ai-Chi Ch'uan.

Paul Abdella
Minneapolis, Minn.
1993

Paul Abdella has been studying and practicing martial arts for 40 years. He has taught T'ai Chi and other styles of martial arts at Twin Cities T'ai Chi Ch'uan Studio since 1990 and has taught T'ai Chi at the University of Minnesota since 1995. Paul also is an artist and classically trained painter. He maintains a studio in Minneapolis, where he paints commissioned works and personal subjects.

Foreword to the 3rd Edition

by Paul Gallagher

It is said that one of the rare blessings in life is to find your perfect teacher. Although Sifu Ray Hayward has the charisma, skill, attitude and perseverance to have attracted numerous world-class teachers, I personally always thought that Sifu Ray's relationship with Grand Master T.T. Liang, his first teacher of T'ai-Chi Ch'uan, was something rare and quite unique.

Sifu Ray (whom I will call "Ray" for the rest of this foreword) and Master Liang seemed to have a special sort of "chemistry," an extraordinary bond characterized by Liang's willingness to impart the depths of his profound knowledge and Ray's sincerity and determination to master whatever he was taught.

One result of this unique alchemy is the book you hold in your hands.

Lessons with Master Liang is so much more than just "another Tai Chi book." It is literally a record of an "Old World" kind of teaching that rarely exists in present times. In an age where much of T'ai-Chi Ch'uan has been relegated to the realm of "health and relaxation exercise," few understand, and even fewer have mastered, its true depth as a martial art—and an art of longevity and rejuvenation.

This book points out the path to both of these achievements in very clear, actionable terms.

Ray Hayward studied closely with Master Liang for many years, took copious notes on every lesson, and audio-recorded many of them. The result is a rare documentation of the most authentic and in-depth teaching of a kind that is rarely found today.

Over a period of more than 40 years I have amassed and read a large collection of books about T'ai-Chi Ch'uan; this one has information that I have not found in ANY other book in either English or Chinese. Typically, traditional masters always withheld the very best of their knowledge, either taking it to the grave with them or entrusting it to one or a few special students, sometimes at the final period of their life.

This book reflects the very unusual situation wherein a master in his prime freely and with utmost generosity imparted the fullness of his teaching to an eager disciple, only hoping that the disciple and his other students could "get it" and ultimately become even better than he was, so T'ai-Chi could become a "whole world exercise" thereby making the world evolve into a "beautiful place."

Lessons with Master Liang is written in the Master's own voice, simply taking direct quotes from Master Liang as he teaches in differing contexts and situations. One of the surprising delights of this book will be reserved for personal students of Liang, who I am sure will "hear" the Master's voice whenever they read this book.

As I read, I could hear Liang's deep and resonant voice as he said the very words that Ray relates in this book. Reading or "hearing" the exact words of the Master gives this

Master T.T. Liang teaching at the basketball courts in the Fenway, Boston, 1979.

book a very special immediacy and impact.

T.T. Liang was the Head Student of Grand Master Cheng Man-ch'ing and as such, received unreserved teaching from Cheng. This book reveals how truly precise and scientific T'ai-Chi Ch'uan really is, both as a method of developing inner cultivation and as a martial art.

There are a number of "treasures" in this third edition that were not revealed in previous editions of this book. There is a description of Liang's "old fashioned" personal training regimen, which is priceless in that most masters almost NEVER reveal their own personal practice methods. The specifics of Cheng Man-ch'ing's unusual "beating the tofu" technique of ch'i development and ch'i projection are exposed for the first time. You will find a description of Liang's formidable manner of practicing head-butting, which was one of his great "secrets" and "masterpieces." And you will discover Liang's technique of post- or tree-training, that was the way he developed powerful Ward Off power everywhere in his body. As if that were not enough, there are expanded sections on such highly sophisticated and rarely practiced skills as Withdraw-Attack and Receiving-Energy, as well as a description of one of Cheng Man-ch'ing's greatest skills: his knowledge of the specific lines whereby he could infallibly discover and displace a person's center of gravity and uproot them at will.

In the latter part of the book, there are stories of Cheng Man-ch'ing's and Liang's experiences and exploits, as well as Liang's teaching on Taoist Meditation, philosophy and ch'i-kung—how to attain perfect health, equanimity and possible "Immortality."

In the end, Master Liang achieved these attributes, passing away in perfect peace at age 102, exactly as he had predicted decades earlier.

This is a book that can be read and reread many times. It embodies the knowledge and accumulated experience of two renowned T'ai-Chi Ch'uan masters, both of whom were scholars as well. This is important since the core writings on T'ai-Chi Ch'uan, the *T'ai-Chi Ch'uan Classics*, were written in classical Chinese, and every character in them is carefully chosen to reflect a precisely nuanced meaning. Supreme mastery of this art is garnered by carefully studying the *T'ai-Chi Ch'uan Classics* and then refining one's practice again and again.

Both Cheng Man-ch'ing and T.T.Liang rose to this level and I am sure Sifu Hayward is not far behind.

In the end of this book, Ray reveals Liang's "Masterpiece," which I know you will enjoy reading about—and even more, applying to your life.

This wonderful book is to be studied, savored, and in the end cherished by any serious student of T'ai-Chi Ch'uan.

Paul B. Gallagher
Western North Carolina Mountains
Season of "Awakening Insects," 2010

Paul B Gallagher has been researching and practicing Chinese Health Arts since 1966. He is the author of *Drawing Silk: Masters' Secrets for Successful Tai Chi Practice* (Book Surge Publishing), and has written numerous articles. He edited *T'ai Chi Ch'uan for Health and Self-Defense* (Random House) with Master T.T. Liang.

Foreword

By Kenneth S. Cohen

Imagine if you had access to unpublished notes of one of the world's greatest sports coaches that included his or her guidelines to Olympic success. Or, as an industrial spy, you learned the proprietary secrets that had allowed your competitor to outsmart you. That may explain some of my excitement when I read Ray Hayward's "field notes" from his years of dedicated study with Master T.T. Liang. The reader should remember that this is oral tradition, words based on both experience and the perceived needs of the student. Don't expect the chiseled perfection of a textbook nor the entertainment of a novel, though Master Liang's dry humor will sometimes have you in stitches. These are words that need to be acted on, put into practice, not stored away for "headucation." For students of T'ai-Chi, this is the most valuable form of literature, similar to the handwritten manuals that, in ancient China, were given only to the most promising students.

When students become teachers, most keep such manuals or notes secret, giving them perhaps a technical and financial edge over other schools. Many boost their egos by keeping students in the dark or implying that there is a light at the end of the tunnel. But the tunnel may take 20 years to cross. Ray Hayward, because he is a teacher with wisdom and maturity, has decided to make his notes public. He knows that the only real secret is "practice." The notes will remain secret if you don't put them into practice. But if, on the other hand, you master the teachings, then you honor both Master Ray and the masters who came before him. Like love, real wisdom grows when it is shared.

I will never forget my own all-too-brief experience with Master Liang. I was introduced by one of his other senior students, Paul Gallagher, my T'ai-Chi colleague and friend. In response to a delightful conversation about Push-Hands and T'ai-Chi applications, the 80-year-old master agreed to demonstrate one of his many *gong*, unique skills. I knew I was being honored because a teacher like Master Liang is not interested in impressing people with *his* ability, but rather in fostering *your* ability. "I want my students to be better than I am," he said. Yet, sometimes a demonstration inspires the student to reach new heights.

Master Liang asked me to stand in my most stable stance. I assumed a T'ai-Chi bow stance, one leg in front of the other with a comfortable length and width. My front foot pointed straight ahead, my rear foot at a 45-degree angle. My weight was shifted to the front leg, knee bent and aligned with the toe, back straight, whole body rooted into the ground. I had used this posture before to maintain balance even when pushed by 250-pound human battering rams! Certainly I could be confident in providing resistance to a lightweight old man. Master Liang assumed a similar stance directly facing me, left leg forward. He raised his left arm to a rounded "Ward-Off" position at the height of his sternum. His left wrist was resting gently against my chest. He then placed a chopstick that he had whittled to a sharp point at both ends between his wrist and chest, so that it was held horizontally in place. I already knew what was coming. Master Liang made a slight rolling movement, dipping and rising a few inches. I was thrown back several feet and hit a mattress standing on the nearby wall with my feet at least a foot off the ground. He had not dropped the chopstick, demonstrating that only body power was used—no push from the arm. And when he removed the chopstick, he showed me his wrist—the chopstick had not left a mark. This means that neither my weight nor my root had caused his arm to press towards his chest. As the T'ai-Chi Classics say: "The energy begins at the feet, rises through the legs, is controlled by the waist, and manifests in the hands." Master Liang had used his perfect posture and absolutely stable frame to transmit the force generated by his feet pressing the ground. It was the ground that was pushing me, amplified by Master Liang's superb understanding of body mechanics and qi. Not only was I unhurt but I was also exhilarated and ready to train harder. I thanked Master Liang for his kindness.

If you are a beginner in T'ai-Chi or related arts, read the book now, but read it again after six months and then again after a year or more of practice. If you are a more advanced practitioner, you will stop periodically to think about and plumb the deeper meanings or return to various sections of the book as you train the skills described in it. And you are committing no sin if you disagree with some of the ideas. Master Liang was fond of saying, "If you believe everything in books, better not to read books!"

I am certain that Master Liang, with his characteristic insight, leaves some information slightly veiled so that the student will have to train sufficiently to understand and earn what he or she learns. As Confucius said, "If I hold up one corner of the paper, and you don't show me the other three, I stop the lesson." Or, there is a Taoist saying: "Knowing when to stop is wisdom." Let me give you two examples, based on my surely limited understanding. Master Liang explains the meaning of three technical terms: T'ing-Chin, Tung-Chin and Shen-Ming. "In Ting-Chin (hearing energy), you feel the muscles stir before your opponent pushes. In Tung-Chin (interpreting energy), you feel the ch'i stir. In Shen-Ming (spiritual insight), you feel their mind stir." Each of these stages obviously requires a greater level of physical, energetic and even spiritual sensitivity. It is the secret of a saying from the T'ai-Chi Classics: "If the opponent doesn't move, I don't move. But if the opponent makes the slightest move, I move first!" How can you move before the opponent? You must catch his/her intent. Now we have the secret, but it is up to us to learn how to diligently train and master it.

Another example: Master Liang tells Ray to find "the line" when practicing Push-Hands. That is, if you wish to upset a person's center of gravity, you must find the place that is stagnant and stiff. If, by contrast, you push an area that is *ling huo*—supple, alive

Master Liang looking over the first edition of Lessons with Master T.T. Liang.

and reactive—your partner will just move out of the way, and you may fall on your face. But what Master Liang is not saying directly is that if the line (which is a straight, angular and "linear" region of the body) is vulnerable, then the opposite, the circle, tends to be powerful and stable. A circle, whether the circular motion of the waist or the circular shape that meets linear force, neutralizes an aggressive attack. And because it is a circle, one turn of the waist avoids the incoming strike and returns fire at the same moment. As I have heard from other teachers, reiterated and elucidated by Master Liang, "In combat, there is no one-two, only one!"

Master Liang's *k'ou chueh*, oral teachings, contain a perennial wisdom. That is, the lessons go beyond the sphere of T'ai-Chi and have relevance to human issues in general. "I am teaching you to yield. I try to intimidate you. If you laugh, you win. If you get angry, I win." Liang sees T'ai-Chi as a way of changing one's temperament, but marriage, he tells us, is even better. You can avoid T'ai-Chi, but you cannot avoid the everyday lessons you receive from your spouse. Hayward's book reminds us that life is the best teacher, and T'ai-Chi is a natural part of life. We are all students; we are all teachers. For Master Liang, "Everyone is my teacher, that's all. I don't want to be a teacher myself; everybody is my teacher." I am reminded of a passage in the Hindu scripture, the *Bhagavad Gita*. The warrior Arjuna does not call God's incarnation, Krishna, his "teacher," but says, rather, "I am your disciple." A scholar commented, "To a true disciple, everyone and everything is the teacher." In accord with this philosophy, Liang neutralized challenges and avoided fights with an attitude of "You are the best;

please be my teacher. The trouble is neutralized." Fools may actually believe that they are thus Liang's teacher. But that is their problem!

I cannot help recounting a similar example of "nonviolent resistance" from my own experience. I was teaching a Yang Style T'ai-Chi class in a park in Boulder, Colorado. At the other end of the park, about 100 yards away, another Yang Style T'ai-Chi teacher was teaching her class. I had always thought that I had a civil, perhaps even cordial relationship with this colleague, so you can imagine my shock when I heard her say, in a deliberately loud voice, "Students, when you know this T'ai-Chi form, you have learned the best. No need to learn other styles or from other teachers. This is it, as good as it gets!" My students looked at me inquisitively and with some obvious discomfort. I immediately rejoined, in an equally strong voice, "Students our T'ai-Chi is the worst. If you want to learn the best T'ai-Chi you should learn from someone else. Ours is the worst!" In Chinese culture, my strategy is called: "Put the egotist on a pedestal of ashes."

Master Liang had many masters and continued to learn and teach throughout his lifetime. He "retired" several times, but then, compelled by eager students, he would start teaching again. My favorite anecdote about Liang's philosophy of lifelong learning concerns my own teacher B. P. Chan. Master Liang was visiting New York City and decided to stop by the studio of his respected colleagues, Masters William C. C. Chen and B. P. Chan. At the time, Master B. P. Chan had just finished teaching an intermediate marital arts class. After introducing the students to Master Liang, Master Chan asked Master Liang, in all sincerity, "Please Liang *Lao shih* (Teacher) would you give me a brief lesson, a few pointers?" Liang tried to refuse, perhaps not wanting the teacher of this school to lose face or appear inferior to a visiting master. B. P. Chan's students were dumbfounded. Chan, seeing the expression on their faces, chastised them. "What's wrong with you? Do you think that I or anyone else knows everything? A fountain of wisdom like Master Liang is here and you don't want to avail yourself of the opportunity? I am ready for a beginner's class!" Hearing this story, I said inwardly, "*P'ei Fu, P'ei Fu*"-Bravo, Bravo. In 2002, Master Liang passed on to the Tai Chi Paradise he so often visited. He was 102 years old. Now thanks to this book, you can continue to train with him. He hasn't retired yet.

Kenneth S. Cohen (Gao Han), author of the *The Way of Qigong: The Art and Science of Chinese Energy Healing* (Ballantine Books), is a health educator and Taoist scholar. He has practiced T'ai-Chi Ch'uan for more than 40 years.

Foreword

My father, known to the T'ai-Chi world as Master T.T. Liang, was the sweetest man in the world. When I was little, I didn't know him that well. He was a traditional Chinese father, loving but aloof. It was hard for him to express himself, show his love for me. But when he was older, he got sweeter every day. He and my mom were fun-loving and always visiting friends. This is what it was like for me growing up, not like a traditional Chinese house. Because my father worked in Chinese customs, my parents went to a lot of social engagements. Not every family was like ours; we were rich at that time. Because my dad was a high-ranking official, he treated people seriously. That was his character; he acted hard outside, but he wasn't inside.

Every week, seven or eight men who were my father's classmates would come to our house to practice T'ai-Chi with my dad. I called them "uncle." My "uncles" would practice in the courtyard all day long. I remember Professor Cheng Man-ch'ing, my father's teacher, coming to our house also. He was very quiet. Because I was a little girl, he treated me in a fatherly way. After my father went to the States to assist Professor Cheng, I spent a lot of time with my mom. She was very quiet, not outspoken, and kept things to herself. But I really got to know her then.

I remember the first time I met Ray in the late 1970s. I went to visit my parents in Boston and Ray came over. He looked like a high school kid. My mom told me a lot about Ray. She took me on the subway. She said that Ray showed her how to use the subway, that he taught her. Ray was like her tour guide. He also helped her learn how to shop. In Taiwan the servants did the shopping, but in America my mother had to do it. She never cooked in Taiwan; she always had a maid. But that changed in the States, too. My mom taught Ray Chinese, and he helped her with English. My mom always corrected him, she force fed it to him.

An-Le and Master Liang in Andover, N.J.

In Boston, the first time I met Ray, I knew he was very special to my dad. My dad treated him like he was a little brat—because he was a little brat! Then we met again when he came and stayed with my parents and me in Minnesota in 1984. Ray stayed for several weeks twice that year, and we got to know each other better. On both visits, I saw how very sweet he was, especially toward my mom and dad. After he moved to Minnesota that summer, I appreciated that he was there for my parents. Ray Hayward is my brother.

An-Le and Ray Hayward, St. Cloud, Minn., 1984.

When I watch Ray do the form, I love it even more than when my dad did it. Ray's T'ai-Chi is beautiful. When my father told you that your T'ai-Chi was no good, he was telling you the opposite of what he really felt. "You are a small fry. I am the big potato." I know deep down inside, though, he thought Ray was one of his best students.

My father explained to us how a discipleship/family relationship works. After passing through a formal ceremony, Ray became my brother. The "Old Chinese" way was that disciples would take care of family members. Ray was closer to my father than Joseph and I, closer than a son or daughter. My brother, Joseph, says that, too.

People will dispute the facts, but I know who my father's disciples are. Ray's relationship with my dad goes all the way back to 1977. He was always there for my dad. He was there for my dad more than I was sometimes. My father had many good students, but he only had two disciples: Ray Hayward and Paul Abdella. I don't know about anybody else. I was there. I remember Ray's and Paul's Chinese disciple names and my father writing their names in Chinese calligraphy on certificates. My friend Amy Roske, who moved with me from Taiwan, was the witness for the discipleship ceremony. We have talked about it many times. She recalls all the details of that ceremony.

In 2002, I came to my dad's memorial service in St Paul, Minn. When I got to the Studio, I was really surprised. The school had set up a Buddhist altar. Monks chanted and led us and all of Ray's students through a traditional Buddhist funeral. It was really beautiful, and all the students doing the Solo Form together at the end was wonderful.

I hope that you get a lot of information from this book and that you see how it really was to learn from my father, T.T. Liang

An-Le "Annie" Liang
November 15, 2010
Year of the Tiger

Rededication

This book is dedicated to my three martial art Grand Masters:
Master T.T. Liang
Master Wai-lun Choi
Master Gin-foon Mark

Acknowledgements

Thanks to Master T.T. Liang for his teachings, guidance, inspiration and generosity. R.I.P.

Thanks to my big sister Annie, An-Le Liang for her forword and support for all these years.

Thanks to my big brother Paul Gallagher for his friendship, teachings, inspiration and for his foreword.

Thanks to Kenneth Cohen, Master Gao Han, for his friendship, teachings and foreword.

Thanks to Julie Cisler for her excellent layout and design of this book.

Thanks to Sharon Nyberg and Emma C. Jerndal for editing the manuscript of this book.

And lastly, thanks to 2nd Generation Master Yang Chien-hou, my inspiration and example of a T'ai-Chi Master. R.I.P.

Introduction

I had very poor health in my childhood, in and out of the hospital with pneumonia and frequent asthma attacks. My health got so bad that my allergy doctor told my mother to get me to do something physical or I would be chronic for the rest of my life. I told my mother that I wanted to study Karate and started at age 13. Karate helped me get control of my health and gave me confidence to pursue Martial Arts training. At some point I read about T'ai-Chi Ch'uan and other Internal Martial Arts, and I became fascinated. I started studying Hwa-Yu T'ai-Chi, and the instructor lent me a copy of *T'ai Chi Ch'uan for Health and Self-Defense* by Master T.T. Liang. This was Liang's first book, which was out of print. After reading the book, I was hooked. After two months of searching (Liang didn't advertise at that time), I met and began studying with Master T.T. Liang at his T'ai-Chi Ch'uan Association in Boston.

Master Liang learned T'ai-Chi Ch'uan to overcome liver disease. After regaining his health, he made T'ai-Chi and other health-related arts his full-time pursuit. He studied many different martial, healing and meditation arts with some of China's legendary masters. Liang had learned English from his British superiors while serving in the Maritime Customs Service in China. His command of English and his vast

Master T.T. Liang with the author in Andover, New Jersey, 1999.

knowledge of Classical Chinese made an excellent bridge for non-Chinese-speaking students. These qualities, coupled with a Bob Hope-like wit, made learning T'ai-Chi from him a delight.

Master Liang is a very selfless teacher, encouraging us to study with many different teachers and learn different styles and methods. He said to "take what is good and discard what is bad." He also reminded us that "no one is perfect." I was introduced to both my Hsing-Yi and Pa-Kua teacher and my 7-Star Praying Mantis teacher by Liang. No matter where my studies take me, I always return to the teachings of Master Liang. His wisdom, knowledge and skill always leave me challenged, yet satisfied.

When I first began studying with Liang Tung-tsai, I heard many stories of the masters fighting and accepting challenges. I was impressed with the idea of subduing opponents. Through the years, Master Liang helped me to see the real accomplishments of the masters. Although they faced either frequent or possible challengers, they had to fight daily with their real enemies: ego, laziness, cruelty, pride and ignorance. After a change of temperament, I could see that greatness in the masters' daily physical, mental and spiritual struggles with their lower selves. Many were great fighters, but the few were great people as well.

Master Liang constantly tells us, "The more you give, the more you will receive." I have close to 100 audiotapes, numerous movies and videos, and four notebooks full of class notes with Master Liang from 1977 to 1993. I always kept my hoard secret and wouldn't let anyone see, let alone borrow from, my treasury. In 1989, I went to London to meet the Sufi Master Shaykh Nazim al-Haqqani. During a lecture he said, "Any knowledge you keep only for yourself is a sin." This statement went deep into my heart. How long was I going to hide my T'ai-Chi knowledge? Shaykh Nazim made an opening for me to see my stinginess and blatant disobedience of Master Liang. I began to share my information with classmates and students, and this book is my first attempt to share it with the public.

This book is comprised of transcribed audiotapes of classes, notes, workshops, lectures and visits with Master Liang compiled from 1997 to 1993 in Boston, St. Cloud, Minn.; Tampa, Fla., and Los Angeles. There are instructions, guidelines, principles, explanations, corrections, stories, criticisms, opinions and advice. My goal is for the reader to use this book to take mini-lessons with Master Liang. I hope to promote the art of T'ai-Chi Ch'uan and the teachings of Master T.T. Liang, not to promote my ego.

Ray Hayward (Shu-kuang)
Fall 2000 – Year of the Dragon

Introduction to the 3rd edition

It's been more than 25 years since I began transcribing notes from the cassette tapes I made at my group and private lessons with Master T.T. Liang. A lot has happened since then. I saw Master Liang celebrate his 100th birthday, and his 101st and his 102nd! I watched how his influence and impact directly affected my life and that of many others. I saw Master Liang's dream, that T'ai-Chi becomes the whole world's exercise, become a reality. I grieved at his death in 2002 and I celebrated my 30-year anniversary of practicing T'ai-Chi Ch'uan in 2007.

I've sold more than a thousand copies of "Lessons with Master Liang." I've received many wonderful notes and e-mails. I received one criticism about which I'd like to comment. One person wrote and told me my book could have been the greatest Tai-Chi book she had ever read because it contained so many insights and such high level information. But, she said, she couldn't call it the best because of the many repetitions in Master Liang's teachings and sayings. This was done on purpose. Master Liang taught in this exact way. He would take a theme or lesson, and then give it over and over again. Sometimes we'd cover the same lesson for weeks. But I noticed that there would always be a little something more from telling to telling. Some facet would be revealed, or I would understand it better just by hearing it told a little bit differently. Or with the passage of time and practice, I'd hear it a little bit deeper. I wanted to keep the quality and style of Master Liang's teaching for the reader, and that is the reason you'll find many versions of the same and similar lessons.

I've included in this edition many additional notes and commentaries. There are a few notes I still keep because of their personal nature, but for the most part, I freely share the wealth I received from my generous and kind teacher.

Ray Hayward
Spring Equinox
Year of the Tiger 2010

A first attempt at a formal portrait of Master T.T. Liang and Ray Hayward, Boston, 1980.

CHAPTER I

SOLO FORM (KUNG-CHIA) AND RELATED PRACTICES

The T'ai-Chi Classics say: "The lowest vertebrae should be plumb erect." If you don't practice T'ai-Chi according to this principle it is not T'ai-Chi. Make sure your hips are tucked under and your spine is erect. Only this is T'ai-Chi's way. Of course, if you do the Solo Form with your buttocks protruding, it's Shao-Lin's way.

First you must have good health. This means that after practicing T'ai-Chi for a long time your health will be perfect. After practicing for a long time you will have a root. You will be firmly rooted. This is called equilibrium. It means that no one can knock you over. When you are standing on two feet and someone pushes you 100 times, you can neutralize it with your waist. You will bend like you are boneless. All the weight will be sunk into one foot. This is called central equilibrium. When you acquire this, we can talk about self-defense.

Slow motion is good for health because, first of all, by practicing slowly, the ch'i sinks to the tan-t'ien and the blood will circulate throughout the body without hindrance. If you use this kind of slow-motion energy, it will come from your sinews and tendons. If you use external force to move your body, it will tense up and your ch'i will rise. This is not good for health. If you practice the slow movement of T'ai-Chi, the energy will gradually penetrate into the sinews and tendons and make the blood circulate throughout the entire body. When this happens, it will really be good for health.

Get this energy from the forms and equilibrium. That means when you stand, no one can push you over. Every day you must practice hard.

The slow movements of T'ai-Chi won't hurt you, no violent movement, which is good for health. Some other "hard" styles may hurt your health. Some exercises are good for health but have nothing to do with self-defense. If you practice T'ai-Chi you can get both. According to my teacher, Cheng Man-ch'ing, T'ai-Chi is 100 percent beneficial for health, not harmful.

So, when you practice, all this is by imagination—by mind, to direct it. So you stand here, you must feel something here, at the top of the head, suspended from above. Some energy is preserved here. Then, swimming in air is very important. You have to do every posture like this, with resistance. Don't feel nothing. You have to feel the air is so heavy, when you shift forward and when you shift backward. Everywhere is some resistance.

Master Liang with R.W. Smith in Taiwan.

You have to feel it. You have to stick to the rule. You practice gradually. You go to the highest standard.

In the Solo Form some postures are double-weighted. That is because you started with your weight on the back foot, then you shifted forward to push and your weight ended on your front foot. Like Fan Through the Back, after you push your opponent you cannot stop the momentum, so you shift forward, ending double-weighted.

When practicing T'ai-Chi, there are many techniques to concentrate on internally. First you have to pick one and use it for one round. Then use another for the next and so on. Gradually they will become second nature and you can concentrate on them all in one posture. Some of these concentration techniques are breathing, application, mind-intent and concentrating on various energy points on the body.

This exercise is really interesting. When they are up to 70 years of age, most Karate and Judo practitioners are stiff and worn out. With T'ai-Chi the older the better, like Johnny Walker Red! The practitioners are old, but still supple and strong. T'ai-Chi is for your whole life. That is like Yang Lu-chan and Yang Chien-hou: Even over 70 they are considered old, but they still become stronger. Their ch'i, everything, is developed because this is an internal system.

❧

Master Liang told me that the correct sequence in training is to practice the form to music, counting the numbers in your head. Then you forget the counting and just do it to the music. Then you add the breath. Then you don't use music, just go by breath. Then you forget the breath and empty your mind. He also told me to feel the air all times. If you don't feel anything, that's wasted practice time. You must feel some resistance from the air, and then your hands will swell and tingle.

❧

Only by practice, gradually you can reach the highest levels.

❧

Don't use energy. You are soft, but still quite strong. Relax; gradually your intrinsic energy will come. Don't use "hand business"; there is nothing to do with hands. Use your whole body as one unit.

❧

Master Liang gave me his personal training schedule. He called it "the old-fashioned way."
+ Five preliminary exercises (warm-ups)
+ Stationary and Walking Ch'i-Kung
+ Solo Form
+ Weapons Forms
+ 2-Persons forms, Pushing-Hands, and fencing with students
+ Post-Practice against the four posts in his basement, 20 times each hand, as follows:
    + Slapping
    + Palming
    + Thrusting
    + Punching
    + Elbow
    + Ward-Off
    + Shoulder
    + Hip-Strike
    + Head-Butt
    + Separate Foot

❧

You get this intrinsic energy from the forms and from rooting. That means you can stand there and no one can push you over. Every day you must practice hard.

According to Professor Cheng, you may sweat a little bit while you practice, but if you sweat more, you should stop practicing. Don't exercise anymore. Too much sweat means your ch'i, everything, is being wasted. If you lose it, you must replenish it. In T'ai-Chi you should reserve—too much sweating can hurt you.

When your hands are swollen and your body is tingling, it feels so comfortable; that means you got something. If after you practice one round you feel tired, that means you are tense. You have to find out your defects, your tension spots.

In the Solo Form you push by imagination. Don't put energy into your body. So you must relax, sink, but don't collapse, don't drop. Collapsed means your blood won't circulate. Be relaxed like a snake, a live snake. A dead snake is collapsed. When you are relaxed, the energy is preserved internally.

Master Liang said the only way to advance is to practice Pushing-Hands every day. Practice rooting and receiving energy too. You must practice the Solo Form smoothly, without jerks or fast movements. When practicing, you must imagine the air around you is heavy. Imagine that every movement is difficult due to the restriction of the air. Without this, you won't advance. When the Classics say, "Mobilize energy as if reeling silk from a cocoon," implies the same principle.

Cheng Man-ch'ing said, "When practicing alone, presume you have an opponent in front of you. When facing an opponent or giving a demonstration, imagine you are practicing alone."

The postures should be widely open, but not to the extreme. They should be comfortably stretched, but not straight or tense.

Try, gradually, to improve day by day. Learn how to move continuously, how not to use jerks, how to be completely relaxed, and then the ch'i will sink. This all takes time. After one round you feel comfortable, ch'i is going to your hands, they are swollen. You can feel it, it is the first step, and the blood is really starting to circulate. Then, gradually, the ch'i must sink, completely sunk to the tan-t'ien. From the tan-t'ien, it issues everywhere. The ch'i should be in the tan-t'ien, and then it will go everywhere. Gradually it goes throughout the whole body, although it is very hard to sink the ch'i to the legs. Try to circulate the ch'i down to the Bubbling-Well point. One Taoist master I knew could do this. I asked him how he did it. He said, "By practicing for 40 years and afterwards by meditation." He would sit in meditation and use his mind to direct the ch'i down to his legs. T'ai-Chi has a very profound theory called mind-intent. That means that where your mind goes, the action immediately follows. That means that ch'i follows the Yi. The ch'i is inside; the Yi is your mind. That means: alright, if I want to strike you with my right hand, immediately I have the intent, then immediately the ch'i will go. That means I call the ch'i; the ch'i is my obedient servant; immediately it obeys my order. If you have not reached that stage, when you call the ch'i it won't come, won't do anything—later though the ch'i will go forward to your fingertips. When you reach a certain level of practice, when the mind-intent orders, the ch'i will be so alert that it will immediately concentrate at the base of your spine and go up and out to your hand.

Keep your body perfectly erect. If you advance or retreat, the whole body goes.

The Classics say: "It appears in the fingers ..." but the energy is issued from the spine. The whole body must be one unit. You've got the idea, but you need more practice. Gradually you acquire a root, and then you go to a higher level. Now your methods are all right, but you have not practiced for a long time. You don't have equilibrium yet. Really, if someone pushes you, if their energy goes to your body, without a root you will be pushed over. You will go backward. If you have a root, you can turn.

Big, medium and small frames refer to the size of the circles the hands make in the Solo Form. For practice, the circles should be wide open, but not to the extreme. This is for health. Big frame stretches your joints and helps to circulate the ch'i. For practical use, your circles should be small, or invisible, to concentrate the energy to a pinpoint. This is effective for pushing the line or for penetrating the body to damage the internal organs. Yang Cheng-fu used big circles, big frame in solo practice, but of course, he used small circles to push. Yang Shao-hou, Cheng-fu's older brother, used the same-sized circles in his Solo Form as he did for practical use, small frame. This small frame can be bad for health, especially for beginners, because it causes you to restrain yourself. The small movements also make the energy come out and is considered hard-style. The height of your stance should be low for all the frames. When you step forward, keep your supporting leg bent so you can exercise it. This will develop your root. If you rise up when you step, you will be lazy and not fully exercise your leg. Cheng Man-ch'ing said that only during White Crane Spreads its Wings do you stand up. We also stand up in High Pat on Horse. Professor Cheng also said Squatting Single Whip is the only posture you go lower. We go lower in Needle at Sea Bottom. All the others you stay the same height.

When practicing the Solo Form, you must pause at the end of each posture. A medium-speed form has a short pause and a slow form has a longer pause. This way, you complete each posture and define it and know which posture is which. Stopping at the end helps to sink the breath, especially during the more difficult postures. When you are doing a slow long form, the pauses are your rest, the "stillness in motion." The mind-intent, the breathing, the rhythm and the applications keep you connected to the next posture. The Classics say: "There should be neither severance nor splice." Severance means stopping at the end of a posture. You spliced it; you joined it to the next posture, making it into one long posture.

Try to make everything correct. Otherwise, if the wrong pattern is formed, it will be hard to change.

When doing the Solo Form, first you have to count numbers as you do the postures. Then, later, you just follow your breath. Soon your five attributes—form, perception, consciousness, action and knowledge—will be empty and you will have an empty mind. This is "meditation in action and action in meditation."

When practicing any of the forms, you must imagine that the air is heavy. You use this imagined resistance to make you use your whole body as one unit. This also helps to develop the intrinsic energy. Your arms will become heavier and you will relax. It does not matter what speed you do the forms; you must always imagine that the air is heavy. Otherwise, you are just moving your hands and it is just like any ordinary exercise.

This is whole life business, this T'ai-Chi. If you get addicted to it, you cannot get rid of it.

The secret to sinking all the weight and concentrating it in the Bubbling-Well point is that when you step forward, your foot should be empty and your leg relaxed. When you shift forward, you still try to keep that relaxed feeling in your leg. Then the weight can sink, and you can have free circulation everywhere.

Your movements must be wide open, yet relaxed. You do not want to make straight, small, jerky movements. They will make you constrain yourself and you will be tense. The way to tell if you are relaxed is at the end of your Solo Form: You should be more comfortable at the end than when you started. Everywhere should be tingling.

When stepping forward, do not come up; try to stay at the same level. This is the way to get a root and is considered an advanced training method.

After you master the counts, counting numbers, then you practice by the music, the beats. After that, you just follow your breathing. Finally, you move automatically, meditating. You can do the Form without music, following your breath, but your movements must be even. If you use the music long enough this will happen naturally. Remember to pause at the ends of the postures and avoid jerks.

"Assimilate the new and excrete the old" means: Breathe new air in and sweat old poisons out. The sweat should be like a light dew covering your body. Too much sweat means you are losing energy.

Eighty percent of my teaching is in my book, *T'ai Chi Ch'uan for Health and Self-Defense.* The rest is in the forms and techniques.

When you practice, try to feel the resistance of the air all over your body, not just the hands and arms. If you do this, you can begin to develop that kind of force-field energy around your body, like the Yang family was famous for.

Once you are relaxed, sunk, and have the principles and breathing mastered, the most important thing to work on is "swimming in air."

Gradually you must develop your own Solo Form, according to your intent and personality. Like Yang Pan-hou: he was very strong and aggressive, so his Solo Form uses a lot of energy. Yang Chien-hou had his soft and hard in perfect coordination, so his Form is yin and yang, soft outside and hard inside. Yang Cheng-fu had a mild temperament, so his Form is very soft, yet firm inside and still good for self-defense.

When we say that Yang Chien-hou's Form has the soft and hard in coordination, it means that if you go lower and slower in your Form, the energy will build inside. So, inside you are quite strong, but outside you are soft. For Pushing-Hands, Yang Chien-hou used soft to neutralize and hard to counterattack, unlike his brother, Pan-hou, who used hard all the time.

One difference between T'ai-Chi and Shao-Lin is that in T'ai-Chi the hands embrace the 8-Trigrams and the feet step in the 5-Elements. Cheng Man-ch'ing told us this. When we asked what it meant, he said, "Even if I explain it to you, you still won't understand."

The body leads the hands. The hands follow the body. The body follows the breath.

You cannot issue energy while curving in your rear foot. This will dissipate the energy. Everything must be ready, and then go.

Practice in the morning, late afternoon and in the evening. Go to bed, get up, and do it all over again. That is the way to succeed.

When you do the Form, imagine the air is heavy and that you feel something at the top of your head, suspending you from above.

When you practice the Form, you should imagine your arms are heavy. This is one of the conditions. Breathing should be done with the abdomen. The ch'i should be in the tan-t'ien. Do not be double-weighted; you have to know this. Do not use jerks, no energy; let your whole body go with each movement. When the body turns, the hand turns. You should feel so heavy; we call it "swimming in air." When you swim in the water, the water resists you; you feel something against you. Practicing in the air, the air is all around! Gradually you will be able to feel it. When you feel it, your hand will be very, very heavy. It will make you more sensitive and the blood will circulate through the whole body.

Cheng Man-ch'ing told me that that is the way the Yang family developed their bodies to be so sensitive. They could feel a punch coming at them from behind.

If you follow my way, first you will have to know the directions, the counts and all the external aspects. Gradually you will master these. Then you work on your breathing—when do you inhale, when to exhale. After you master the breathing you forget it, but it happens just the same. Then you will be in a trance—meditation in action. You do the Form by intention. The way is to forget everything. After you finish, you think, "Oh, I'm here already." That

is complete relaxation of mind and body. That is the highest level. Can you do the Solo Form like this?

In the beginning, you can go up and down in your Form. According to Cheng Man-ch'ing, in White Crane you stand up, and in Squatting Single Whip you go down. All the rest stay the same height. If you want to go higher and lower, this means you want to be lazy, rest your legs. If you stay low, it is difficult. If you come up, that is easy. Professor Cheng told me that. Beginners may take it easy, but gradually you have to stay the same height; the whole body can go up a little at the end of some postures, but not by physical action. You use intent to rise. So, everything should be directed by the mind. It has nothing to do with energy. If you use energy, you cannot use your mind. The mind directs everything by imagination, everything like that. If you use energy, not the mind, you cannot go to a higher level. Like Cheng Man-ch'ing, he was so soft, but when he issued energy it was like a sudden explosion, like a bomb. Cheng learned from the Yang family. During his whole life he never learned hard-style. Only through the soft-style did he reach that high level. It is not easy, really something remarkable.

Now you know this Solo Form. Externally it is okay, but internally a lot of things you have to remember. Externally the postures may be quite correct, but internally quite incorrect. Something may not be quite right. You must presume that you have an opponent in front of you. Some energy must be at the top of the head all the time to suspend it. Also, use intrinsic energy, do not be double-weighted—a lot of things. So many places in your body you have to relax. You have to know how to breathe, at what point do you inhale or exhale, what time to push—a lot of things you have to know.

⇛

If you practice this Form, it will tell you how to yield.

⇛

After you learn something, you must gradually change it to your own way. Blind followers are dead; they do not do their own style. Rebels can get something. Learn what you can, take the best, and make your own way. Otherwise, you will only get a low level. Look at the Yang family, each one had their own breakthrough. None of them did their Form like the other, but the principles stayed the same.

⇛

I give you the general idea, and then you practice according to this way. Keep the lowest vertebrae plumb erect. Swim in air. Don't be double-weighted—whole body as one unit. Don't turn the head and body in opposite directions. Don't lean forward. All the postures do correctly, not like dogs walking. Step like a cat—step first, and then shift the weight.

⇛

No need to correct the postures. I just want to see your form and the principles.

⇛

When practicing any of the T'ai-Chi forms, you must imagine the air is heavy. You use this imagined resistance to make you use the whole body as one unit. This also helps to develop the intrinsic energy. Your arms will become heavier, and you will relax. It doesn't matter the speed of the form; you must always imagine the air is heavy. Otherwise, you are just moving your hands and it is like any other exercise.

⇛

Yang Chien-hou's Solo Form was hard inside, but soft outside. You can do the Form as you like, as long as you follow the Classics.

⇛

Master Liang practicing Single Whip in the Botanical Gardens in Taipei, Taiwan

Anyhow, try to relax. Make your whole body like cotton, like an iron bar wrapped in cotton. The iron bar is the bone and the outside is cotton. Don't be stiff—don't collapse. Inside is very sensitive and alert. When the outside is soft, you can hear the opponent's energy. Otherwise, you are just a piece of wood.

❧

Every posture you must stretch it out, but not to the fullest extent.

❧

Anyhow, health is the most important thing. Everything should be the natural way.

❧

So, anyway, you have your own way of doing things. Don't rely entirely on teachers. You must find your own way. If you rely entirely on teachers, better not to have teachers.

❧

This Praying Mantis is really good. You must study some hard-style so you can have the soft and hard in coordination.

PUSHING-HANDS (T'UI-SHOU)

At the lowest level of Pushing-Hands, you have to use some energy to make the opponent have a defect position. Then you can push them over.

There are so many things to learn in Pushing-Hands, then your attack will be effective. So, you must practice with all these conditions, otherwise it will be of no use. When you practice T'ai-Chi, go very slowly, but when you use it, it's very fast. Other systems emphasize the use of the hand, so they use the hand to neutralize. T'ai-Chi is different from all the rest because it emphasizes the whole body and the intrinsic energy. As soon as you neutralize, you attack. This is a very fast action. I remember when I would practice with my teacher and he would push me far away. I would watch him as he pushed, but I couldn't see his hands move; they didn't stretch. He would always explain that you must use intrinsic energy. At first I couldn't do what he told me. I didn't know what intrinsic energy was. He would say that if I didn't believe him, he'd push me again. Then he would push me far, far away. Again, I couldn't see his hands move. The Classics say: "You have hands all over your body, but it has nothing to do with hands." That means you have the function of your hands with every part of your body. You can feel, grab and strike-everything with every part. "Nothing to do with hands" means you don't generate power with your hands. This is the way of T'ai-Chi.

Hearing energy is to feel the energy. So when someone touches you, you will immediately "know" them. You know their action or intent; this is hearing energy. There is no sound, but you hear it. At their slightest stir, you know their yin and yang and will be able to react with this energy. You will know the real from the unreal, meaning whether the opponent is feinting or really attacking. When you hear their energy, you will know what direction to neutralize just by how they touch you. Your hands and body are so sensitive and alert. You will know whether their energy is strong or weak.

According to my teacher (Professor Cheng), the most important posture for Pushing-Hands is Roll-Back. When you push me and I can't retreat anymore, I must neutralize with Roll-Back. When you push me, I must deflect your energy to the side, not let it get to me. If I don't turn, you will push me over. This posture is very important. When you completely have this technique, half the mastery of Pushing-Hands is done. This means your T'ai-Chi technique will go higher.

"Withdraw means attack." Sometimes you have to push as you neutralize. Maybe you can neutralize the first push, but not the second. So you have to prevent the second attack by countering the first attack.

✍

Touch the body first. Then withdraw, and then push. You must "know" me first.

✍

When you practice Pushing-Hands, you must know your partners' yin and yang, the hard and soft. When you touch them and they feel soft, or yin, don't push or you will fall into a trap. If, when you touch them and their body is hard, or yang, don't worry, just push. If you don't test the yin and yang, it means that you don't know them.

✍

Cheng Man-ch'ing would gesture at tofu with a chopstick, using the whole body and trying to issue ch'i from the end of the stick to the tofu. After practicing, he would eat the tofu. If it was sour, that meant that the ch'i was transmitted to the cake. That is why we practice with weapons, so that we can reach the tip with our ch'i. When we can get energy to the tip of a weapon, it is much easier to get to the hands.

✍

When you touch someone's body, you must seek out the straight line, otherwise they'll neutralize you. Straight lines cannot be neutralized.

✍

Neutralizing energy means to get rid of your opponent's energy when it comes to your body. Their energy cannot touch my body. This is accomplished by yielding.

✍

Master Liang demonstrating the application of Fair Lady with his disciple, Paul Abdella.

Then, next go to Pushing-Hands. First you have to learn how to lose. A good one can go backwards, head touch the ground, immediately go upwards. That means the body is so soft, just like a willow tree. This is first—learn how to yield. Sometimes you'll be pushed very hard; you must respond exactly, so soft. Then next, we must teach you how to counterattack. Counterattack is not so easy. You have to know which hand to push with so as to avoid double-weighting. You have to know the center of gravity, the lines for concentrating on when you push. Everywhere must be completely relaxed before you push. All the energy is concentrated in one direction. If you put energy on someplace, that part of your body is tense; that means you have to deduct that energy from the 100 percent of your pushing power. You want it all to go out. Also, when you push, it must be like breaking a dry and brittle stick. All go at once. That's the way.

Train and condition the parts of your body for striking. Let them get used to it all, so you won't feel pain. Train it in T'ai-Chi fashion by not using energy and by relaxing. We call this T'ai-Chi post-training.

What to do if they don't attack, if they don't move? If somebody is really good, they will wait for you to move. Then you have to make them move first. You can press them a little bit and observe the reaction. Cheng Man-ch'ing's way was to wait for you to push, let you come to him. He didn't care; he'd wait.

Force and energy are different. Force comes from the bones, but energy comes from the sinews and tendons.

Master Liang and Joanne Von Blon demonstrating Pushing-Hands during a seminar in 1994 at Twin Cities T'ai-Chi Ch'uan Studio in St. Paul, Minn.

You must practice against a tree. That way, when you strike someone, you won't hurt yourself. If you hit them and you are hurt, that's not the way.

The first thing you have to know in Pushing-Hands is how to yield. Losing is very important. Don't begin the study of Pushing-Hands with attacking. Don't use force against force, this is first. Try to lose. Small loss, small gain; big loss, big gain. Gradually you will be able to keep your partner's energy away from your body. First is rooting. Second is neutralizing. Last is counterattack.

If you push the center of gravity they cannot turn in any direction. Find out the center of gravity to control them. It's very hard to neutralize if your center of gravity is pushed.

Just train every day hitting the post; make your striking areas stronger. Then you can stand it. So sometimes I can knock down a student with my head. As soon as they see my head, they are afraid because I really hit with my head. They feel pain, knock them down. Train hitting the post every day. Formerly I trained every day against a tree, but not as much now. But still my technique is effective.

Use the turning of the waist to turn the hand palm up in Roll-Back. If you just use hand strength, it's called a "hand block" and is double-weighted.

In Pushing-Hands, if I hold you, you must neutralize it. You have to get out of my grasp. Pull is one of the eight postures and must be neutralized. If someone grabbed any of the Yang family, they would give you a shot of electricity. Their internal energy would come out of their wrist, hurting your hand and making you let go. You have to practice the grasping and escaping exercise. As soon as I hold you, before I can pull, you must get out of my grip.

Attacking energy means to use a counteroffensive technique on your opponent. You must use intrinsic energy and the techniques of the yin and yang, center of gravity, etc. Prolonged-energy, abrupt-energy, sinking-energy all depend on the action of the opponent. To prolong means to take your opponent a long, long way. Then sometimes, you must use a jerk. Just suddenly go. Then sometimes you have to go further. It all depends on your opponent. If they resist, you must use the short technique. If they don't, then you just push them for a longer time. Corkscrew-energy will directly penetrate their body. Nothing will appear externally, but internally there will be injury.

In T'ai-Chi, the first step is to get equilibrium or a root. This comes from the Solo Form. The second step is Pushing-Hands. First, you learn how to lose, not to gain— further developing your root. When someone pushes, you don't resist. Don't be like bulls fighting—yield. If you cannot yield, then let them push you over. Don't resist. Gradually you will be able to neutralize all your partner's attacks. The third step is to learn how to find the line: Where is the center of gravity, where is the soft and hard, how to concentrate your whole body as one unit. These are called the "techniques" of T'ai-Chi. Don't be double-weighted; don't use just the hand. After pushing, the hand remains in the same position, not stretched forward. This way you prevent a grab from your opponent.

When practicing Pushing-Hands, from time to time change the hands and feet to develop the whole body.

Ray Hayward demonstrating Neutralizing Energy, top, Rooting Energy, center, and Receiving Energy, bottom.

In Pushing-Hands you must be closely connected together with your partner. Don't leave any gaps. When you're being pushed it's not necessary to take the initiative. Let them push you. See what they're going to do. At the last moment, turn and neutralize. Lead them to that extended position. When they are forward, let them come farther, then immediately turn. If they aren't really all the way forward and you turn, that means you took the initiative. Induce them to fall into your trap, then turn. Of course, if they push immediately, you must turn immediately, no need to continue retreating. When two people are just practicing, they must go back as far as possible. One goes forward as far as they can. Go back until you can't stand it anymore, and then turn. This fully exercises your legs and makes your body soft. Your legs will become so strong that you will have equilibrium. If you don't go back as far as possible, you won't work your legs fully. Then when a strong partner pushes you, you'll fall down. So, you must push your partner as far as possible to be exercised yourself. When the waist becomes flexible, it's like a willow tree bending 100 times in the wind. In Taiwan, there are some people who, when you push them, their heads go back and touch the ground, but their roots are still there. They are firmly rooted, yet so soft. So, when you practice, let your partner push you.

Push without going forward. All I need is to touch my hand on your body, but I don't need to come forward because I want to keep my equilibrium. Otherwise, I'll put myself into a defect position. The push power is mobilized from the leg first, from the foot into the leg. Then it's issued from the spine.

If your weight is on the right foot, you must push with your left hand to be single-weighted. If you get an opportunity to push but you are doubled-weighted, you have to shift your weight first before you push so you are single-weighted. This way you can properly use your intrinsic energy. Your bow-stance should not be too long in Pushing-Hands, so you can shift back and forth easily and quickly.

Don't use hand-business. Use your whole body as one unit.

One way to practice is for two people to place a staff on each other's stomach, and then shift back and forth, alternating pushing and neutralizing. Afterward, when you strike me, I can do like Yang Cheng-fu who would absorb your whole fist. Then, when you try to pull the fist out, you cannot withdraw because your opponent is holding it with their stomach. When you use force to try to pull your fist out, they'll release all their energy and knock you down.

Go back as far as you can. If your partner's reach is long, retreat as far as *you* can go.

When practicing Pushing-Hands you can really hurt somebody because when you push your opponent's body, some of the energy can go into the internal organs. T'ai-Chi's energy is internal. When you use it, the ch'i can bypass the outer part of the body and go inside, hurting the organs seriously.

Don't lean against the post. This is called, "don't hang your dead meat on me. I am not a meat hook." Don't rely on the post to stop your push. Use your front leg to stop you. The back leg is for power, front leg for a brake.

Don't do too hard, too much. Try to gradually develop your energy. Practice T'ai-Chi to make yourself stronger and stronger. Afterward you can stand the opponent's energy. Everybody's nature is to have some part of his or her body not quite normal. You must be careful. Don't work too hard or too strenuously. I know one man in Taiwan, he is very good. His art is beautiful. One time a man who was very strong pushed him down, hurting him inside. It made him bleed. So now his art can't go to a higher level.

If you push me and I can't neutralize, I must jump like a tiger.

You have to know where the center of gravity is. If I'm on their center of gravity, they cannot escape; this very important. Each person has a center of gravity. Even if they are small, or if they are taller than you, you have to find their center of gravity. He or she smaller, you taller; you have to push down through the center of gravity. You smaller, you push up through the center of gravity. If they are on that place, you must do something. You cannot withdraw; if you withdraw, they knock you down. You can use receiving energy, even if they're on your center. That's a technique (receiving energy) if you can do it correctly. It must be withdraw a little bit, withdraw-and-attack we call it. You cannot immediately go when they push. When they push 70 percent into your body, only 30 percent left, you issue energy to utilize the 30 percent and push them over.

Don't be too anxious. Don't hurt yourself.

If you practice Pushing-Hands two hours per day for one year, you will get something. There is no other way but constant practice. That's the rule. Develop your intrinsic energy.

Pull is used when the opponent is in a defect position. You can't use it if they are in perfect balance. When pulling your partner, don't pull near to you. Otherwise, you will pull them into you and they can use Shoulder. Their whole body will go to you. So, unbalance them, and then pull to the side.

When pushing, you must find the center of gravity, the proper place to push.

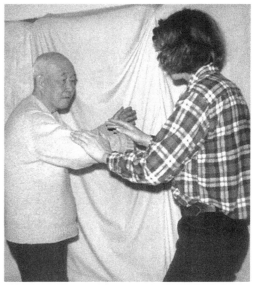

Master T.T. Liang and disciple Ray Hayward in November, 1977, at the Boylston Street Studio in Boston. Ray was 17 years old and a junior in high school.

Don't hit the post with your hand energy. This defeats the whole-body training. Also, if you are too far away, don't stretch the hands to make up the distance. Use your waist and legs. This is excellent distance-training.

In Pushing-Hands, lock elbow to elbow to control them.

If your opponent is pressing you in your center of gravity, you are in danger. You can't tell which direction they are going to press. In the 8-Trigrams (Pa-Kua), the most dangerous one is K'an, which corresponds to your center of gravity. If you are pushed there, you cannot turn. The only way to escape is to go backwards. If I find your center of gravity, you are in danger. Any direction you turn, I can follow you and knock you over. Sometimes this means I catch your center of gravity, just the middle of your body. The shoulders are too high, the hips are too low. Then, you can turn in any direction, I don't care.

When your opponent attacks you, you must know their direction; if it is a real or false attack, you must know their energy. You only get this from experience. Otherwise, you can't use 4 ounces to deflect 1,000 pounds. To know which way you should move (neutralize), you only get from practice and experience. Then you'll know it exactly, instantly.

By practicing the Solo Form, you will have a root. That's very important. That's not my own philosophy; it's T'ai-Chi's way. You must get equilibrium. Then gradually you will be able to be firmly rooted, able to sink. Then you learn all the techniques like lines, center of gravity and how to concentrate. You learn all these things—how to push out and how to use this energy issued from the spine. When Cheng Man-ch'ing would push me, I didn't see his hand move or stretch out. Sometimes he would shout when he pushed me. Cheng said that when Yang Cheng-fu pushed him down, he couldn't get up. He didn't see Yang's hand move either. The reason the Yangs were so good was because they didn't have to work, just practice all day long.

If I push you and you can't stand my energy, then jump backward.

Through experience, as soon as you touch your partner's body, you will have everything you need to push them over in your mind. Like a painter painting bamboo, you have in your mind where you start painting. As soon as I touch you I know where the line is, where your center of gravity is—everything is in my mind. Then when I push, there's no mistake. If you don't have these conditions in your mind, then it's a blind push. So, you have a certain method, a technique, a way. As soon as I touch, I know. This is called Tung-Chin (interpreting energy); it means I know you, I interpret you. I know you, you don't know me. I know all the conditions for a successful attack. It is clearly in my mind, concentrated. As soon as I touch, I know whether or not I can push you over. When my fingers just touch, I know. This is Tung-Chin. If I don't touch, how can I know? If we are far apart, I don't care. Gradually, when you touch, you'll know. You'll be able to sense the yin and yang, solid and empty. When you touch someone and they are so soft, no energy, that means they have something. You must take care; otherwise you'll fall into a trap. If their body is stiff as hell, don't worry. If their body is soft and relaxed, you must be careful. Try to make them stiff, and then you can push. So we have to test. When your hand touches, then you'll know.

Cheng Man-ch'ing told me about the lines. You think anybody knows about it? I don't think so. None of my teachers know it. Only Professor Cheng used to push me so terribly. He knew the lines to push. Anybody wanting to learn about the lines must go to Cheng. The line is very important. All these techniques Cheng got from Chang Ch'ing-ling, not Yang Cheng-fu. Only Cheng said don't push into the root. You must push a little bit to either side. When I pushed with him, he said, "Avoid my root."

Which foot holds the weight determines which hand you push with. When you push, don't go forward. All the weight goes into the ground through your front foot. After you push, your weight shifts forward, being careful not to let the front knee go over the toe. That way you won't fall over. If you push and stretch your hands forward, your knee will naturally go over the toe. If this happens, you will become unbalanced—a defect position. Mostly the energy comes from the spine. If you know all the theory, then there's nothing left, no other method except practice—only by constant daily practice. One day you'll get it. Then you read the Classics, studying one sentence, one by one. This is the correct way. The Classics say to issue energy from the spine. There is nothing to do with the hands. What does that mean? Gradually you will understand it has nothing to do with hands. The hands are really relaxed—it's whole-body energy. The energy is sharp, sudden; we call it dry and brittle energy, like breaking a dry stick or biscuit. The energy is tremendously powerful when it comes. If you use hand energy, you can progress up to a certain level, but you'll stop there. Hand energy makes your body tense. Your ch'i will rise and you will pant. After issuing intrinsic energy 100 times, you'll feel nothing. You won't use much energy. With this energy, after gradual practice, one day you will arrive at a high standard. So the Classics say: "From the most soft and yielding, you will arrive at the most powerful and unyielding." That means you go to the extreme end, then the opposite will come.

As soon as a little bit of energy really comes to your body, don't forget and use hand-business to try to neutralize them and throw them away. T'ai-Chi way does not use hands.

When using Roll-Back, it's the body that neutralizes the push. Don't use the hand. Don't be too concerned about having your arm pushed against your body. You have to trap your opponent. Induce them to overextend. So go back as far as possible and let them push your arms against you; it will only draw them closer and unbalanced.

When shifting the weight forward in a bow-stance, let the energy go downward, and then you'll have a root. Don't let your leg energy go forward. Your knee should not go over the toe when you shift or push. Don't follow the opponent with your knee when you push. This is floating, the opposite of rooting.

If someone had stiff arms when practicing Pushing-Hands with Professor Cheng, he would pull or push them through their arms.

The Yang family has a saying, "In Ward-Off, don't let your energy go to the opponent's body. In Roll-Back, don't let the opponent's energy come to your body." This means: When attacking, don't let your hands stretch toward the opponent; when neutralizing, don't let them push you over.

Having a root is when you can stand in one spot and nobody can push you over. You can stand and resist or you can neutralize without falling over. Both feet are glued to the floor. One foot is rooted 3 feet below the ground. To get a root, you must practice T'ai-Chi twice per day, paying careful attention to the shifting of weight from one foot to the other. You must pay particular attention to maintaining the same height throughout the Form. When you do the postures, you must be relaxed and sunken deeply. The legs must be bent and the postures low.

The only way to advance is to practice Pushing-Hands every day. Practice rooting and receiving energy too.

Master Liang at a seminar in Minneapolis in 1985. Ray Hayward, right, demonstrating 4-Directions Pushing-Hands.

In Pushing-Hands, if you step in after you push, it's more effective. When pushing with two hands, don't step in or you'll be in danger of leaning forward. Only step in when you push with one hand. If you use two hands, you must remain in a fixed-step. Beginners use two hands to push, but advanced people should use one.

&ᷓ

Neutralize and counterattack in a circle is best.

&ᷓ

In Pushing-Hands, don't lean on the opponent. Even before pushing, don't lean. "I'm not a meat hook, don't hang your dead meat on me" means the same thing.

&ᷓ

When shifting the weight forward, the root goes 3 feet into the ground. That way you can't lose your balance when pushing forward. This also prevents the opponent from pulling you forward. When shifting backward, imagine the opponent's pushing energy goes through your body, through your root and into the ground. This way you won't fall over when using Roll-Back.

&ᷓ

Your body must be erect or you can't counter the counter.

&ᷓ

When you finally get intrinsic-energy, you don't know it. Then one day you use it and push someone far away.

&ᷓ

Don't push the opponent blindly. You must touch them lightly first to find their center of gravity, then you must test them or "question" them—use a little bit of energy to "feel" them. If, when you touch them, you feel them tense up and resist you, withdraw slightly to make them fall forward. Then either pull them or merge with the opponent's retreat and push them. If they resist strongly, you have to use more energy to make them lose balance. This technique is called Withdraw and Push.

&ᷓ

If, when you touch your opponent, they are soft, then you must be careful and use a more delicate technique. If, when you push forward, your opponent neutralizes by sinking back, you must be careful not to overextend. You must use the front root and let your weight sink 3 feet into the ground.

&ᷓ

If your opponent resists you with stiff arms, you can use Withdraw-Attack or Pull or Split to make them lose balance. Cheng Man-ch'ing would push right through the arm to get to the body and knock them down.

If the opponent lifts their foot to step in or just lunges in to push, there are two ways you can counter. If you see their foot lift or you anticipate their lunge, push forward quickly and catch them off-balance. If you don't see the lunge and they invade your territory, pivot to the side to avoid them and push them sideways.

Master Liang in the early 1960s.

When practicing Pushing-Hands, your bow-stance shouldn't be too long. If it is too long you can't shift weight easily or step quickly if need be.

The time to use Pull is when the opponent is in a defect position and has lost their balance. If they don't lose their balance, don't use Pull.

When pushing the opponent's arm, you must control the wrist and elbow; otherwise, they might hit you with one or the other.

In Roll-Back, go back as far as you can, then turn. Induce them to come forward and overextend. Roll-Back is called: "Open the door and let the robber come in." If you don't open the door, you can't catch them. Let them come in; entice them to fall into your trap. At the last moment (of the push), when you can't stand it anymore, turn.

If you're in a bad position, a ready-to-be-beaten position, don't stay there. Adjust your legs and waist and immediately turn and correct your position and make your opponent have a defect position.

The best way is to go back as far as possible. Some of Huang Hsing-hsien's students could bend backward and touch the ground with their heads, then immediately get up. So, when you practice, shift and bend backward as far as you can go so you can exercise your root. This is called "learning how to lose" and "investing in loss." Gradually your legs will become so strong that you will have a root. There is no shortcut way. Don't be afraid to be pushed over by someone. Let them push you over so you can strengthen your legs.

There is a technique called "Stealing Steps." When Pushing-Hands with an opponent, you can sneak inside their territory by bringing your rear foot up and stepping forward with the front foot to push. The counter is that when you see or feel the rear foot come up, push forward quickly while they have a short base (stance).

If you are suddenly pushed, you must use Roll-Back and turn right away. If you go backward, you'll be finished. It all depends on your opponent; you must follow. Suppose you let them come in, you must go backward. If they suddenly push, you must suddenly turn.

A lot of Shao-Lin people practice Pushing-Hands, but they don't do it according to T'ai-Chi's way. They use Ch'in-Na. You have to know some Ch'in-Na, otherwise you'll be caught. In Taiwan, I saw some advanced T'ai-Chi people who were caught in Ch'in-Na. You must get away before they lock your joint.

If your opponent is too far away, don't try to catch them; otherwise, you will overextend and lose balance.

When pushing with one hand, you should control the opponent with the other hand. Use Push-Pull if the opponent is too far forward, but if they are in good position, you can't use Push-Pull. If you punch at me but are still in a good position, I can't use Push-Pull. If I withdraw and induce you to overextend to hit me, then I can use Push-Pull.

If you squat down to avoid my push, the question is what time do I push you? When you go down, I give you no chance to come up; I merge my push with your squat. Suppose I don't do that. Then you get me when you come back up. I give you no chance to go up.

When you have a root, you can direct your waist to turn and bend to neutralize. If you don't have a root, when you bend or turn you will fall over by your own action.

When T'ai-Chi strikes the opponent, we touch the body first and then use energy. If we use the fist, we touch and then use energy. Sometimes we can turn the fist and use "corkscrew energy." If we want to strike with the palm, we touch first with the fingertips and then we can slam down the palm. The kicks don't touch first, but we touch or grasp with our hand before kicking. You can strike from a distance provided you are touching with another part of your body. We touch first so we can know the opponent's yin and yang and can strike the substantial, not fall into a trap.

When using the folding technique, you are like a snake. No matter how hard they try, they can't keep you outside their guard. Some technique (strike) is bound to get in, you just keep changing.

When you know what the opponent is going to do before an attack, you have acquired "interpreting energy." When you know at the slightest stir, you have "hearing energy." When you can detect the energy before it fully comes to you and avoid it, you have "neutralizing energy."

The Classics say it (intrinsic energy) appears in the fingers, but the energy is issued from the spine, from the whole body as one unit. You've got the idea, but you need more practice. Gradually you get a root, and then you go to a higher level. Now your methods are right, but you haven't practiced a long time. You don't have equilibrium. If you don't have a root when you are pushed, you'll go backward. If you have a root, you can turn.

In T'ai-Chi, we don't use the hand to block. If someone strikes you, you have to avoid the strike. Try to neutralize or turn, don't just use the hand to block. This technique is a very

Master Liang at a seminar at Deer Mountain Taoist Academy in Vermont. J. Richard Roy, an instructor and disciple in Liang's lineage, is seated front row, second from left.

scientific, logical way. If someone really hits you, you must turn, grasp them and then counter. If they have a weapon, don't block—you'll be hurt. Try to turn it away, let them go by. That means 4 ounces deflects 1,000 pounds. Gradually, automatically, you'll neutralize that way.

No other way—just talking theory is no use. Two people must practice; after a long time, suddenly everything will be right and you'll have something. You have to know how to correctly counterattack. These things are from two-person practice. Gradually, as soon as you touch someone, you'll know whether you can push or not. All my words are from Cheng Man-ch'ing. Nobody can explain so well, in so much detail, as he can.

Don't anticipate. When you are being pushed slowly, go back as far as possible. Don't turn immediately, don't take the initiative. You listen, wait, and don't take any action of your own. Don't try to lead them where they aren't pushing. If they are more advanced than you, you'll be in trouble. Feel where their energy is going, you have to find out. If the opponent doesn't go, you don't go. If the opponent goes forward, don't just turn as you like or you'll get caught. Don't move. If they turn, you turn. Maybe they will try a fake or feint. If you're not following, you won't know. Sometimes the first push is a fake or a setup for when you turn to neutralize. When my energy can't touch your body, you've got something. You have to know my intention, what place I am going, how to neutralize it. What is the meaning of neutralize? To neutralize is to attack. When you neutralize, your appropriate hand goes forward (to counterattack). Of course, if we are practicing one side attack, one side defend, you don't do it. Still practice putting the hand there, ready, that means I want to push you.

You have to form this habit; otherwise you are ready to be beaten all the time. Immediately go, neutralize and push at the same time, not one, then two—just one.

There is also use of the foot. The foot techniques are important: sweeping, tripping, and all these techniques. If you sweep me, I lift my foot to neutralize, then step in and push.

"Borrowing energy" means you use the opponent's energy to uproot them. It is the same as "receiving energy." When using "withdraw-attack energy," you use your own energy to counterattack.

When pushing the chest, if they neutralize by bending backward, push diagonally downward. There is no need to change the hands to the stomach. When pushing the stomach, if they neutralize by sinking backward, push diagonally upward through their stomach to uproot them. No need to change the hands to the chest. This is called "going through the yin to get to the yang."

Master Liang said in Pushing-Hands, whoever is softest will win. If you are more relaxed than your partner, you will be able to sense their intention. Also, the more relaxed you are, the more energy you can generate to counterattack.

In Pushing-Hands, make sure you have no tension in your hands and arms. That way you'll be able to sense and detect attacks.

When the masters say "adhere means to pull up or dislocate the opponent's center of gravity," it means that you have to touch the opponent first and then uproot. If you push from a distance, hit-pushing, you can't uproot. That is the way Shao-Lin practitioners push—hitting into the opponent. You can't "know" your opponent's yin and yang with that method and you won't be able to control the direction of your push, especially if they turn as you hit-push. You won't be able to change the line.

If you are put in a defect position, off balance, you have to immediately turn to get into a superior position. You cannot effectively push if you are in a defect position. Of course, if you are pushed while in a defect position, you have to turn or neutralize.

When two people are practicing with a mattress against the wall, the side facing the wall should push like hell, don't worry. The side with their back facing the mattress should try hard to neutralize. If you can't neutralize, just go back into the mattress. Then switch sides.

Keep the body facing straight forward, using the back leg like drawing a bow to issue energy. When you push forward, your body should be relaxed. Don't put a lot of energy on your upper torso. Your ch'i should be in the tan-t'ien. Don't use hands, otherwise you will feel tired.

The line is very important. Whether or not you know how to find the line, that is the big question. This is a technique, a condition. Without techniques, whoever is stronger will win. When you push, if he or she turns, immediately change and find another direction to push. If he or she pushes low on your body, you have to adapt to follow. Closely attach to them. Don't let them control you. Get rid of their hand. Don't allow their hands to go anywhere they like on your body. Protect yourself.

First of all, your whole body should be relaxed. When you push forward, use intrinsic energy. Your body should be perfectly erect. Don't lean forward.

You must have a root. A root—you must have it. When Professor Cheng pushed me, his hands were very soft. His hand would touch you, the energy would come out, but the hands stayed soft. His hand was like nothing, no energy at all, but the energy that came out was terrible. At the last second, his whole body would go with it, but no energy was put on his hand. Sometimes he knocked me out.

Your hand must touch my body entirely, and then go. Don't let your hand be stiff; it should be soft, nothing.

You must find the line, exactly on the line, then push with the whole body. Make your push sharp, like dry and brittle energy. Touch first, then go.

Your stance, or base, shouldn't be too small; otherwise, it is easy to be pushed over. It should be big, but not too big; otherwise, you cannot get up to follow (step). So, not too big, not too small. Try gradually to go back as far as you can, then let them push you over, don't resist. That is the way of training, then you will be so flexible, then you will have a root. No other way. Practice. Don't be afraid to be knocked over. To lose—not to gain. Small loss, small gain; big loss, big gain.

The question is how it happened, how your opponent's hand suddenly comes to this place? That means a surprise attack; you have to find it out. What's wrong is that you let the hand go down to push you, you didn't know it. You didn't closely attach, adhere. Don't give them a chance to push. Be careful. You have to lock elbow to elbow.

Well-wishers gathered to say farewell to Master Liang when he decided to "retire" and move to Minnesota. This was taken in front of Liang's studio at 16 Peterboro Street, Boston. Paul Gallagher is in the back row, fourth from the left.

So far, so good. If your partner is hard-style, likes to push hard, let them push. Gradually you'll know how to neutralize.

The 18 ways are the 18 directions, or lines. Cheng Man-ch'ing told me these things; I still can't understand all of them. I know 11 or 12; Professor Cheng knew 26. He said the Yang family originally had 18. Anyway, when I push you, in any direction, with any method, there are 18 ways to push you over. I asked Professor Cheng to teach me how to push the line. He would show me, but when I tried, he'd always change.

In Pushing-Hands, it is not good to duck down to push forward. If your opponent knows something, they will push diagonally downward on you when you squat. Your pushes should be fast. From yin suddenly go to yang, and then immediately back to yin. The Classics say: "Storing energy is like drawing a bow—issuing energy is shooting an arrow." Master Liang said, "How can you shoot an arrow slowly? It's either in the bow, or it's gone, so fast."

In Pushing-Hands, there is a technique about territory. If you come into my territory, I must push you out; otherwise, you are close enough to push me. You must know each other's territory. If I go into your territory, you must be careful and protect yourself; otherwise, you're in danger.

We have a posture called Roll-Back. That means to let the robber in, then catch him. If you don't let him in, you can't catch him. If you let him in and don't catch him, he'll steal everything!

When Master Liang was learning from Cheng Man-ch'ing, he would bring his notebook to class. When someone was knocked down or uprooted in Pushing-Hands, Cheng would come over and explain why and how it was done, and the appropriate defenses. Master Liang recorded 11 years of such classes.

Master Liang said not to use too much energy when deflecting a push or strike because a sensitive person will use the energy of your deflection to change their direction or technique. If you deflect their hand too hard to the outside, they will circle around and go inside.

"To neutralize is to attack" means that you take advantage of the push (yang).

Master Liang said one reason for the name "bow-stance" is that when you push, the action and feeling is like drawing a bow with your feet or legs.

In Ting-Chin (hearing energy), you feel the muscles stir before your opponent pushes. In Tung-Chin (interpreting energy), you feel the ch'i stir. In Shen-Ming (spiritual insight), you feel their mind stir.

This Chan Su Chin (silk reeling energy) is very important for Yang Style T'ai-Chi. The basic meaning is to have the postures be smooth, like reeling silk from a cocoon. To use it for practical use means that it's like binding your opponent before you knock them down or hit them. You can twist their body like in Pushing-Hands to bind them before you push, or you can seize their joint and strike like in Ta-Lu or San-Shou. You must wrap them up like coiling silk.

You must reach the stage where you have "hands all over your body, but nothing to do with hands." Don't push with hand energy—the body pushes. The hands only support the push.

When you neutralize, you must store up (inhale). When you counterattack, you must exhale or you will be hurt inside.

When you get intrinsic energy, you feel it is effortless to push somebody, but they go far away. When you push, you must exhale to let the ch'i go out and the whole body to go back to soft. If you are countered, your inside won't be hurt, or if you are knocked down, you won't be hurt. The ground is hard, but you are soft, so no injury. If hard hits hard, the hardest wins, which, of course, is the ground.

The willow bending exercise is most important—this I must stress. This trains the yin and yang to be in coordination. When you push, I go back. When you go back, I go forward. Neutralizing is Pushing-Hand's way. You must go back as far as possible and make your body soft, sensitive and alert.

How to practice Chieh-Chin (receiving energy): When your opponent pushes you with 70 percent of their energy and there is 30 percent left, we utilize this remaining 30 percent to uproot them. Receiving energy is not so easy. Try to practice this energy with a small movement. This is very useful but not so easy to develop. I learned this from Cheng Man-ch'ing. His "receiving energy" was very good. We use the standard exercise for this, the same way the Yangs practiced. If 100 percent of their energy comes to you, you'll be knocked down. You let 70 percent come in, then issue your energy and you'll have a push of 130 percent. Let 70 percent come into your root, then issue. Use your firmly rooted posture to uproot them, and then go. There is no other way to get this energy except to practice—practice every day.

Reasons to practice against a post/tree:
1   Condition the striking area, get it used to it
2   Train not to use hand-energy
3   Learn to be single-weighted
4   Distance training
5   Train correct stances and weighting
6   Train alignment
7   Works on "suddenly appear, suddenly disappear"
Master Liang said to practice T'ai-Chi's way, in T'ai-Chi fashion, using the whole body as one unit. Liang used to practice Elbow, Shoulder and Ward-Off 100 times each, everyday, against a tree.

So many teachers don't know how to neutralize. They just push, but don't care about defending. First, try to lose, not to gain. Try to push each other like hell. Gradually your body will become softer. After you can neutralize, you can talk about pushing someone over. This art is not force against force. The most important thing is what? You must have equilibrium! You can just stand there and no one can push you over, but don't use it. Just like you have atomic bombs, but don't use them. So anybody trying to push you over should be neutralized. No resisting. Gradually, from big circles, you'll use smaller circles to defend. You neutralize, then immediately go. Not like bulls fighting! Yang Lu-chan only relaxed to neutralize, then he would immediately issue energy to counterattack. These small circles can become invisible.

Don't just practice with one partner. Everyone has a different method to push. You have to learn how to adapt to all kinds of situations.

Striking the T'ai-Chi post is the same way as knock the tofu. Whole body goes with it, relaxed.

Neutralize their strong side and attack their weak side. Try to be aware of the strong side, but don't worry about the weak side.

For beginners, they must learn not to take the initiative. They must learn to lose. Beginners must follow, but mostly they don't want to do it that way.

"Adhere" can mean sticking when going forward. "Join" can mean sticking when going backward. "Follow" means responding to your partner's movement, like retreating when they advance. "Stick" can mean actively staying in contact.

So when you are pushing, at the last moment you have the intent to push upward. Go forward. At the last moment, have the intent to go up to uproot them. Push forward, and then go up. Have that intention. Don't always push straight forward, uproot them. This is called uprooting. Not using the hand, you use intent. What is intent? By imagination. Intent and imagination are the same. Go upward and your opponent will naturally go upward. Did you see the picture of Cheng Man-ch'ing uprooting William Chen? The technique is to push you up into the air, then knock you down. No other way but practice, practice.

Master Liang said Cheng Man-ch'ing told him that both Chapter 11 in the *Tao Te Ching* and the proverb about "opening the door to let the robber in" describe the technique of Roll-Back. Cheng said you use the arm to protect yourself and the space between your arms and body to trap the opponent. He said the arms were like the walls of a house. They protect you from the weather and also can keep the robber out. The inside is where you live, the space. Sometimes, if you're not home, the robber can get in. So you have to use the inside to trap the robber. If you don't let him in, you can't trap him or catch him.

Master Liang and Ray Hayward demonstrate "Hammer" for an article in T'ai-Chi Magazine, 1984.

If you let your opponent hold you, and you push them into the sea or off the cliff, they'll pull you with them.

If you push with two hands, you remain in a fixed stance. If you push with one hand, you can have your rear foot take a half step forward after you push. This is called "follow-step." You can only follow-step if you are single-weighted. When you are pushing, at the last moment, have the intent to go up to uproot them. Push forward; at the last instant, go up. Have this intention. Don't always push straight forward. This is called uprooting. Don't use the hand, use intent. What is intent? Push by imagination—intent and imagination are the same thing. Go upward with your intent and they will naturally go upward. In Peking, Yang Cheng-fu would practice in the park. He would hang nets in the trees. He would push his students up and into the nets. This is uprooting. You must push upward. Did you see the pictures of Cheng Man-ch'ing uprooting William Chen? Once he pushes you up into the air, it is easy to knock you down. It will really hurt you.

Cheng Man-ch'ing said, "If you do the Solo Form correctly, gradually your art will improve. If performed incorrectly, even if you practice for your whole life, it's no use." He also said, "I took responsibility; this is the foundation." Of course, when you learn the other things, Pushing-Hands and weapons, you can improve but only to a certain extent, then you stop there. If you use force against force you can improve, but gradually you'll stay there. You cannot reach a high rank. When you advance using T'ai-Chi's principle, a kind of energy is developed that takes you to higher and higher levels. So, the basic fundamentals, the principles—you know them, and then you have to practice according to them. This is the right direction.

Master Cheng Man-ch'ing rooting the push of four people. Robert W. Smith is the second person pushing.

Master Liang was asked one time about practicing Pushing-Hands for tournament competition. This meant using a lot of rules and regulations and competing in an aggressive manner. After explaining this to Master Liang, he was asked if we should start practicing this way. He said, "The masters didn't do it that way."

After practicing Pushing-Hands with Professor Cheng for more than 10 years, I got to the point where if I was only defending, he couldn't push me over. Many of my senior classmates reached this level. This is because Professor Cheng taught us about rooting, neutralizing and defending. If we tried to attack or counterattack, then he could still easily knock us down.

My classmate Wang Tze-chung said he practiced the "knock the tofu" technique. He came to Boston to challenge me. As soon as he came, I knew he wanted to challenge me. Why would he suddenly come to visit me? If this fellow suddenly comes here, must be something. He said he came to try Pushing-Hands with me, see how I am, what my level is. I said, all right and I told my wife to come and be the witness. I told him if you can push me over, I will pack up and retire. So he tried to push me. I tried to root. He said I had a very strong root, he could not push me. All right, next is my turn to push him. As soon as I push, he falls over, three times. I pushed three times, he falls three times. Wang said I had a root, okay, but I was not up to Professor Cheng's level. Sometimes when someone is pushing very seriously, their hand comes so fast, their whole body comes to you, and you have to help yourself by your equilibrium. Because sometimes, when he pushed me, his energy really came to my body. The only thing I could do is root. I can resist a little bit. Otherwise, I'm finished. I resist, and then turn. Really, his energy had already come to my body. I resist, then immediately turn. Because I use this root to resist him, I used my equilibrium to help me a little bit. Otherwise, if I don't have it, I'll fall over. That is what is meant by "from the most soft and yielding comes the most pliable and unyielding." You use this root. To acquire a root, no other way except you practice every day. Don't double-weight when doing the Solo Form, this is a root. You have a root here, in your legs. When you walk, don't fall into your steps. Wait a little bit between stepping and shifting, keeping weight only on one foot. You have to concentrate on one foot. Like the photo of Professor Cheng Man-ch'ing, four people stand in front of him pushing, no one can push him over. How he can reach that stage? I read so many books, learned from so many teachers. They all say the same thing: there is no other way except daily practice. Practice the Solo Form then one day you have it.

CHAPTER III

TA-LU
&
SAN-SHOU

Ray Hayward and Master T.T. Liang demonstrating San-Shou at Paul Gallagher's Deer Mountain Taoist Academy workshop and seminar, 1988.

Free-hand techniques, or San-Shou, are found in the Two-Person Dance. First you learn Pushing-Hands in a fixed manner. Then you start adding techniques from the Solo Form and the Two-Person Form. From Pushing-Hands you start to learn to defend against pushing, kicking and sweeps.

❧

In the Two-Person Dance, turn the palm up in every Roll-Back. Even if the push isn't real, you must train it to have the habit and to show this technique.

❧

In the Two-Person Form, if our partner pushes our arm against our body to try to control us, we must turn to neutralize the push. If they hold our wrist or arm, we must sink to get out of their grasp.

❧

I learned the Two-Person Form from Mr. Hsiung Yan-hou. He learned from Yang Chien-hou. After I learned from Mr. Hsiung, I added the Yang family's Ta-Lu, Wang Yen-nien's Ta-Lu and Cheng Man-ch'ing's Ta-Lu. I also put in horizontal, vertical and fixed- and active-step Pushing-Hands and made a formal beginning and ending. Altogether there are 178 postures.

Master T.T. Liang practicing T'ai-Chi San-Shou with Lin Chun-fu in Taiwan.

Liang and Lin work on Tui-Shou and San-Shou in Taiwan, 1976.

❧

You should learn both sides of the Two-Person Form, that way you can adapt to all circumstances. When you can do both sides, you are on your way to mastering that form.

❧

Every posture in the Two-Person set (San-Shou) consists of three movements done in slow motion: neutralize or hua, hold/seize or na, and strike or da. So when you do it, you have to know that when someone strikes you, you must first know how to neutralize them, then how to hold them and then how to strike or counterattack. But you cannot do this well unless you have been practicing a long time. How to neutralize just in time? How to hold and how to strike? When you strike, you must know how to find your opponent's defect position and your superior position, their center of gravity, the lines and other things. So when practicing, do this well, this Two-Person Form. When it comes to practical use, you can use this form.

When the three parts of a posture are separated, it is a dance. When the three parts of a technique are combined into one, it becomes one knockdown or knockout. So practice for a long time and get all the techniques so that when you practice all the 150 postures singularly, you'll know what each one is. You'll know the practical use of each posture. So when you practice singly, you'll presume that you have an opponent in front of you. Then you have something in your mind to base them on when you practice. Otherwise you have nothing to base it on, and gradually your form will be changed, and all the practical use will be lost. So practice Two-Person Dance, and you can master the form and Pushing-Hands as well.

T'ai-Chi for self-defense is whole life business. It takes practicing year after year to get anything. Even ten years is only a short time to practice.

By using set counts for the Two-Person Form, you give each other warning so you can know when the technique is coming.

My teacher, Hsiung Yan-hou, learned the Two-Person Form from Yang Chien-hou. The reason not too many people know San-Shou is because when Yang Cheng-fu was locked in a room for four years, his father, Chien-hou, had only gotten through teaching him the postures, the Pushing-Hands and Ta-Lu, and the Spear practices. Shortly after Cheng-fu was released, his father died, before teaching him the Two-Person Form. So, only direct students of Yang Chien-hou know San-Shou.

Master Liang and Ray Hayward partner in a T'ai-Chi San-Shou demonstration in Boston, 1979.

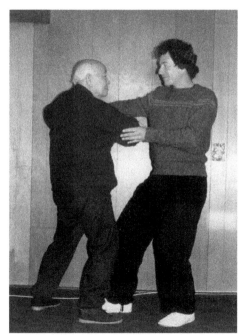

Master Liang and Ray Hayward doing T'ai-Chi San-Shou in St. Cloud, Minn., 1984.

In the Two-Person Form, make sure you don't randomly go into the opponent's territory. Keep them out of your territory and only invade their territory if you have a chance to attack.

In Cheng Man-ch'ing's Ta-Lu, I pull you and you follow me using Elbow, then Shoulder. I use Roll-Back, then Slap. You use Ward-Off to defend, and then Pull. To neutralize the Shoulder you have to use Slap (Split) to drive me off.

Now practice Ta-Lu. Formerly, in Pushing-Hands, you use four movements: Ward-Off, Roll-Back, Press and Push, mostly in a fixed stance. Now you use the other four movements: Pull, Split, Elbow and Shoulder, mostly in an active-stepping method. So, Ta-Lu and T'ui-Shou (Pushing-Hands) are very helpful practices.

When using Shoulder-Stroke, there are two methods. When using Shoulder to strike with, you mostly use the front of the shoulder. For Pushing-Hands, we mostly use the side of the shoulder. When you use it, the whole body goes forward, not the shoulder. This is T'ai-Chi's way. The most serious way is to use the shoulder to strike the heart. Like a hammer, use the shoulder to hit the heart.

In the Two-Person Form you must clearly distinguish between Hua (neutralize), Na (hold) and Da (strike). My Da is your Hua. For practice, it must be broken down to learn the principles and techniques. For practical use, the three movements become one. So, when you practice, make yourself neutralize, then hold, then strike. Don't try to hold or strike right away.

Cheng Man-ch'ing's Ta-Lu is a perfect example of "folding technique." You fold from Palm (Split) to Elbow to Shoulder. Pull neutralizes Slap, Roll-Back neutralizes Elbow, Slap neutralizes Shoulder.

Hsiung Yan-hou learned T'ai-Chi from Yang Chien-hou. I lived with him in his home for six months to learn his Solo Form, Two-Person Form, Sword and Sword Fencing. I had to sleep on the floor, eat only vegetables and meditate daily because Mr. Hsiung was a devout Buddhist.

Master Liang stressed the application of the lower fist in the posture Strike Tiger. That is why we punch to the kidney in the same posture in the Two-Person Form.

Ray Hayward and Paul Abdella demonstrating T'ai-Chi San-Shou for Master Liang in NJ, 1998.

Master Liang, right, practicing T'ai-Chi San-Shou with Lin Chun-fu at the Botanical Gardens in Taiwan.

Withdraw-attack refers to a T'ai-Chi technique. Withdraw-adhere refers to a T'ai-Chi principle. The principle means that when the opponent withdraws, I adhere or maintain the same distance, body to body. If they advance, I neutralize and attack. Adhere means maintaining the same distance. Join means to connect to the opponent. Stick means to be touching them. Follow means to move according to their posture. No resistance means not to attack when they are attacking, or force against force. "No Letting Go" means not to let them unstick themselves.

T'ai-Chi is not like other martial arts. In T'ai-Chi, you have to study as much as you practice. T'ai-Chi is the "Scholar's Martial Art."

In the Two-Person Form, you must look at your partner, look into their eyes. You must be on guard against their strikes. You also activate your spirit of vitality by watching your partner.

I changed the Two-Person Dance to go in a circular pattern. Formerly it went back and forth in a straight line.

❧

By practicing by yourself (in the beginning), you can't get the techniques. The Two-Person Form has all of them in it. But it's still not the real one. When you practice the postures singly, then you'll get it. Through Pushing-Hands you get experience: how to neutralize, how to attack. Gradually, practicing faster, your techniques can be used for fighting.

❧

Master Liang taught us that in the martial arts, there is a training theory called the Three Centers. The center can be looked at as if it is the opponent,

Master Liang and Ray Hayward demonstrating T'ai-Chi San-Shou in St. Paul, Minn., 1988.

or the opponent's centerline or center of gravity, or where the action is happening. Basically it is three strategies defining attacker and defender. Hsing-Yi emphasizes going through the center, or the opponent. Pa-Kua emphasizes going around the center, going around the opponent. T'ai-Chi emphasizes the maintaining, or being the center. T'ai-Chi is in the middle, following, neutralizing and attacking with invisible circles. Master Liang also said that every style utilizes the Three Centers.

❧

Ta-Lu practice is good for Pushing-Hands. Wang Yen-nien's Ta-Lu goes straight in practice, but to the corners in the Two-Person Form.

❧

You should learn some hard-style, then gradually you utilize the two styles, and then you follow the soft-style, like T'ai-Chi, Hsing-Yi or Pa-Kua. I asked Cheng Man-ch'ing why he didn't learn Hsing-Yi or Pa-Kua. He said, "T'ai-Chi is in the middle. Where the opponent goes, you follow." Wherever they go, you face them; this never gives them a chance to attack. Suppose you circle me like Pa-Kua style. I follow you, facing you wherever you go. You make a big circle, I make a small circle. Suppose you circle and I don't follow. I will get into trouble. If you circle fast, I must turn fast.

CHAPTER IV

WEAPONS TRAINING

Master Liang with his sword teacher, Li Chien-fei. Liang's daughter, An-le, is to his left.

In T'ai-Chi Knife (Sabre), when using the drag-step, don't let your rear foot come too close to your front foot. Otherwise you'll lose your base. The drag-step is to compensate for the momentum and weight of the knife. The drag helps keep your body erect, not leaning forward.

❧

In the Sword Form, most of the time you look at the point. This is for concentration. From the practical side, you look at the tip because that is where your opponent is.

❧

When practicing T'ai-Chi Sword or Spear, keep your eyes focused on the tip. This keeps the spirit of vitality alive and helps the mind-intent send the ch'i to the tip. When practicing the T'ai-Chi Knife, most of the time you look in the direction the edge of the knife is cutting, but sometimes you look at the tip.

❧

The reason we practice with weapons is so we can reach the tip with our ch'i. When we can direct energy to the tip of a weapon, it becomes easy to get it to circulate to the hands.

❧

Double Swords with Tassels was Master Liang's favorite weapon form.

❧

In T'ai-Chi Sword, you must watch the point to extend the ch'i to the tip. Most postures you follow the tip wherever it goes. Some postures you look forward to your opponent. Your

Master Liang and Barbara Root in a photo shoot for Liang's 1977 edition of T'ai Chi Ch'uan For Health And Self Defense.

wrist must be relaxed, and you hold the sword with your thumb, middle and ring fingers. When your hand is palm up, you open your hand slightly, only holding with three fingers. When the hand is palm down, you close your hand, but it is still soft and "hollow."

Why do you want to learn all these weapons? Because once you master all the hand forms, you must go next to the weapons. You have to learn to extend your energy, everything, to go from the body, to the hand and out to the tip of the weapon. Don't use hand-business; the whole body goes with the weapon. So, when you practice, try to send your energy into the weapon and make it vibrate.

Tai Chi Sword Dance (With Tassel)	Bea
1 Preparation	2
2 Step Forward & Unite The Sword	2
3 The Immortal Guiding The Road	2
4 Triple Bracelets Enticing The Moon	4
5 The Chief Star of The Dipper	3
6 The Swallow Wadding Through Water	2
7 Intercept & Sweep (Right Style)	2
8 Intercept & Sweep (Left Style)	2
9 Junior Star of The Dipper	2
10 The Wasp Entering The Hive	2
11 The Vigilant Cat Catching The Mouse	3
12 The Dragonfly Sipping Water	2
13 The Swallow Entering The Nest	5
14 The Phoenix Spreading Both Wings	2
15 The Whirlwind, Right Style	3
16 Junior Star of The Dipper	2
17 The Whirlwind, Left Style	4
18 Fishing Style	2
19 Poke Grass & Search For The Snake, Right Style	2
20 Poke Grass & Search For The Snake, Left Style	2
21 Poke Grass & Search For The Snake, Right Style	2
22 Embrace The Moon	1
23 Send The Bird To The Bush	1
24 The Black Dragon Wagging Tail	2
25 The Wind Rolls Up The Lotus	4
26 The Lion Wagging Head, Right	1
27 The Lion Wagging Head, Left	1
28 The Lion Wagging Head, Right	1
29 The Tiger Embraces The Head	2
30 The Wild Horse Leaps Over The Mountain Torrent	2
31 Turn Over Body To Check The Horse	1
32 The Compass	1

	Bea
33 To Brush Off Dust Against Wind, Right	2
34 To Brush Off Dust Against Wind, Left	2
35 To Brush Off Dust Against Wind, Right	2
36 To Drift With The Current	3
37 The Meteor Pursues The Moon	2
38 The Sky Lark Flies Over The Waterfall	1
39 Raise Curtain Posture	2
40 Left, Right Cart Wheel Sword Dance	3
41 The Swallow Holds Mud	1
42 The Roc Spreading Wing	2
43 Drag Moon From The Sea Bottom	1
44 Embrace The Moon Again	1
45 The Rhinoceros Peeps The Moon	1
46 Shoot The Wild Goose Posture	1
47 The Blue Dragon Stretches Claws	1
48 Phoenix Spreading Both Wings	2
49 Right & Left Crossed Intercept	2
50 Shoot Wild Goose Posture	1
51 White Ape Offers Fruits	2
52 Flowers Falling Posture	6
53 Fair Lady Weaving At The Shuttle	5
54 The White Tiger Twists Tail	3
55 The Carp Leaps Over The Dragon Gate	4
56 The Blue Dragon Twists Pillar	5
57 The Immortal Guiding The Road	2
58 The Wind Sweeps The Flowering Plum	2
59 Holding The Tablet	2
60 Embrace The Sword To The Original Position	4

The T'ai-Chi Sword Form written out by Master Liang and photocopied for class.

You know this sword is not used like hard-style. Because the sword is so sharp, there is no need to use a big stab when a little one will cut you. All you have to do is nick your opponent; that's enough. You don't need to penetrate to the other side of their body.

Why do we practice weapons? When we practice empty-handed, we get energy to the extremities. With weapons we get energy to the tip. Then our hand-energy is stronger.

The Sword Fencing is the same as Pushing-Hands. You must know about each other's territory. If you are too close, you are in as much danger as your opponent. You must keep the right amount of distance.

Neutralizing a push is like Spear practice. You can aim his or her push off course right away. That way, if they try a sudden attack, you'll be protected.

Master Liang showing the three basic movements of T'ai-Chi Spear.

❧

My art is with the Classics, the music, and the tassel.

❧

T'ai-Chi Sword comes from Wu-Dang Mountain through the Taoist priest, Sung Wai-yee. He taught the Yang brothers, Pan-hou and Chien-hou.

❧

When practicing Solo T'ai-Chi Spear, you are developing energy for issuing. When practicing the Two-Person Spear sets, you are developing sticking energy for neutralizing. The sets should be practiced in a straight line and in circular fashion.

❧

In the Sword, don't use hand-business. You put the sword near the target, and then issue short-energy to stab or cut. This is the fundamental theory or principle. At the last moment, go. Only Cheng Man-ch'ing told us this so many times. You look at his Sword Form, so soft. We asked, what is this kind of sword? There is no energy used—nothing. He told us it is not necessary to use energy. That means you get close, and then use energy. Not from way back to stab forward. Don't use energy all the way, just the last moment. The last moment is enough; that kind of energy must be developed. Use your whole body, not just the hand. Gradually intrinsic

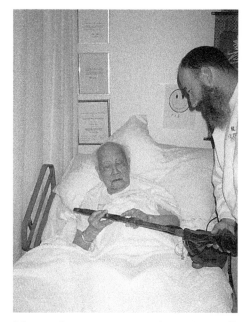

Master Liang examining Ray Hayward's antique T'ai-Chi sword.

energy will be developed. You see my hand, the sword is nearly dropped, but it cannot fall out. It looks loose, but you cannot knock it out of my hand. That is the principle; gradually you'll do it according to this way. It looks easy, but it takes 10 years to reach that level.

I learned Wu-Dang Fencing from Mr. Chi Ch'ing-tze. His book has a lot of discrepancies. So I asked him and gradually learned the whole thing correctly.

In sword practice, the sword, body and head should be in one line. Use the waist for horizontal cuts and the rear leg for stabs.

Master Liang's favorite form was Double Swords with Tassel, which he choreographed.

Weapons training becomes more important than empty-hand training only after you can circulate energy to the hands. Then you must try to circulate, to extend, your energy to the tip of the weapon.

The Chien (sword)—the tip is so sharp. No use to swing it like a sabre. You get near, then issue. Get near to the target. Use sudden energy, not swinging energy. That means I get near you, then I cut you. Not from far away to cut you. This is the fundamental principle. You have to realize it; then you'll make it short energy. At the last moment, go. Anybody ever tell you these things? I don't think so. I learned weapons from so many teachers. Only Cheng Man-ch'ing told us this. You look at his sword: nothing there. He said it is not necessary to use energy. Don't use energy, only at the last moment. At the last moment, intrinsic energy comes. It is not from the arm, like Shao-Lin style. The last moment is enough; that kind of energy should be developed. Don't hold the sword tight. Gradually you'll do it according to these principles. It makes a big difference. You have to look at the point; imagine someone is there. Once you know all the postures, the names and applications, you'll really have something. You'll reach a high rank. Use your intent, your imagination; don't use jerks or hand-business. These are the principles. So far, can anybody do the Sword like that? No. Most are stiff. So, if you practice according to the principles, the same as Wu-Dang Fencing, it is a more scientific way. Of course, the Sword helps with Pushing-Hands. You learn that the energy must come from the body, out to the hand and out to the tip. When the energy goes to the point, the sword will shake, will tremble. The energy is so powerful; the shaking can knock the weapon out of your opponent's hand. The vibrations start small, gradually getting bigger. The same principle applies to the Knife and Spear, not from far away.

If you want to develop your pushing power and you don't have a partner, you must get a long spear (stick). Get one about ten feet long and I'll show you how to practice. The weight and length will make you use your whole body. This will help you practice issuing energy.

I asked my teacher why he used a tassel on his sword. Formerly, this teacher was famous for using the sword in Shantung Province. When he swung the tassel, you didn't see his hand move; he used whole body energy like T'ai-Chi. After, I learned Sword from him. He was an excellent man; his art was beautiful. His name was Li Chien-fei.

San-Tsai Fencing is learned first. Then you learn T'ai-Chi Sword Fencing. Then you learn Wu-Dang Fencing, which is the most advanced.

Master Liang and Ray Hayward demonstrating San-Tsai Sword Fencing in Boston, 1979.

CHAPTER V

T'AI-CHI CLASSICS

The Yang family's secrets are mostly the Classics put into common language.

There is no other way to advance except by constant practice. You won't even know when you've improved to a certain level. When you reach a certain level, it will be hard to improve and progress is slower. Then you go another step, you'll learn more and you'll keep going. Then you'll get to a certain level—you can't go higher. Then you must study the Classics—find out something, and then you can go further. Otherwise you'll stop at one level. You must always study, always try to find out more from teachers, books and the Classics.

Chang San-feng is the founder of T'ai-Chi Ch'uan. Afterward, Wang Chung-yueh developed it further. First, there were only a few postures. Then Wang Chung-yueh developed the art and made more detail. The three most important Classics are Chang San-feng's and the two by Wang Chung-yueh. If you know these, you'll really know what T'ai-Chi is. Wang took Chang's Classic and made it more comprehensible. Wang "completed the musical performance," making it more detailed and easier to understand.

Double-weighting applies to moving only. In the Two-Person Form, Ta-Lu and some standing meditation, you have your weight 50/50 in a horse-stance. When you move, your foot should be empty, then step. Your weight can be sunk in two feet until your opponent attacks, then you have to shift the weight to one foot. As long as you're not moving you can stand any way you like. Double-weighting applies to moving and pushing. If your weight is on the left foot, you must push with the right hand—that is correct. If you have your weight on the left foot and push with the left hand, that is double-weighting. The Classics say: "T'ai-Chi springs from Wu-Chi. It is the source of motion and tranquility, and the mother of yin and yang. In motion they separate, in tranquility they fuse into one."

It only takes four ounces to make your opponent have a defect position. The Classics say: "Four ounces to deflect 1,000 pounds."

The Classics say: "No severance and no splice." This means for Pushing-Hands, don't break away or lose contact with your partner. Also, don't push when he or she is pushing, "splicing" the pushes together.

The Classics say: "If you want to pull up, first push down," that is like trying to pull up a strong weed or small tree. You must push down and pull up, until it is loose and unstable. Then you can remove it.

Don't double-weight when doing the Solo Form. The Classics say: "From the most soft and yielding comes the most powerful and unyielding." This is about rooting. When you walk or do T'ai-Chi, don't let the weight rest on two feet; you have to concentrate only on one foot. Like Cheng Man-ch'ing, five people standing in front of him pushing, he can't be pushed over. He can resist. How can he reach that stage? I've read so many books, studied with many teachers. All said, there is no other way except daily practice. Practice the Solo Form, then one day you'll get it. Then practice Pushing-Hands, then weapons.

The Classics say: "Yin does not leave yang. Yang does not leave yin." That means you know what percentage of your opponent's energy is coming to your body. It

Master Liang and disciple Ray Hayward at the Deer Mountain seminar, 1988.

This formal portrait was taken of Professor Cheng Man-ch'ing's senior students after a practice session at Master Liang's house. Some of the T'ai-Chi "uncles" are in the back row: Tao Ping-siang, fourth from left; Enoch Yu, fifth from left; Joseph Liang, sixth from left, and William C.C. Chen, second from right. Liang is at the center of the front row. At his right is Mrs. Liang, with daughter An-le Liang on her lap.

is referring to interpreting energy. That means interpreting energy is the art of knowing how much, or what percentage of energy, is coming to your body. When the Classics say "to withdraw is to attack," it is another way of talking about interpreting energy. That means when you feel their energy, you withdraw to unbalance them, then attack. Interpreting means knowing their body—is it hard or soft—to know if I should push or not. So, interpreting is knowing your opponent's energy, whether it is coming out to attack you or remaining inside them.

Using four ounces to deflect 1,000 pounds means you use four ounces of energy to turn your body so all of your opponent's energy goes to the side. Then, when they are off balance, you use your energy to knock them down. If, after you neutralize, they are still in a good position, you can do nothing. This technique is different than "receiving energy." In receiving energy, you let 70 percent of the energy come to your body, you withdraw a little to unbalance them, then utilize their remaining 30 percent to add to your own pushing energy. Four ounces defeating 1,000 pounds means not letting any energy come to your body. Receiving energy, you let 70 percent come to you; if more comes, you must neutralize.

The Classics say: "From T'ing-Chin (hearing energy) you go to Tung-Chin (interpreting energy). From Tung-Chin you go to Shen-Ming (spiritual insight)." Shen-Ming, or perfect clarity, is the highest level where you can know your opponent's intentions from a distance. Like when Yang Lu-chan knew the Shao-Lin monk was coming to try a surprise attack on him. Shen-Ming is also knowing events before they happen, like Yang Chien-hou knowing about his death three hours before. This is true spiritual ability.

"To withdraw is to attack" means sometimes you have to push someone as you neutralize them. Maybe you can neutralize the first push, but the second is giving you trouble. So you can use this technique to prevent a second attack by countering the first push.

The Classics say: "The energy is like steel refined one 100 times over." That means the more you practice, the more relaxed you'll be. The more relaxed you are, the sharper and stronger your intrinsic energy will be.

The Classics say to keep the back straight and erect. Don't lean forward—that's called excess. You must relax the chest and tailbone.

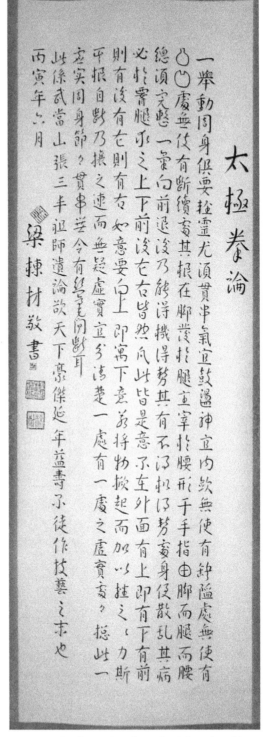

An example of Liang's calligraphy, T'ai-Chi Ch'uan Classic by Chang San-feng

T'ai Chi Ch'uan Classic
Chang Sen Feng, 13th Century
Translation and Calligraphy by T. T. Liang

In every movement the entire body should be light and agile and all of its parts connected like a string of pearls.

The Ch'i should be stimulated and the spirit of vitality should be retained internally.

There should be neither deficiency nor excess, neither hollow nor projections, neither severance nor splice.

The energy is rooted in the feet, develops in the legs, is directed by the waist, and move up to the fingers. The feet, legs and waist must act as one so that when advancing and retreating you will obtain a good opportunity and a superior position.

If you fail to gain these advantages, your body will be in a state of disorder and confusion. The only way to correct this fault is by adjusting your legs and waist.

The same principle applies to upward and downward, forward and backward, left and right. All the movements are to be directed by the consciousness within, rather than by the appearance without.

When attacking above you must not forget below; when striking to the left you must pay attention to the right; and when advancing you must have regard for retreating. If an attack is proposed upward, the initial intent must be downward. If you want to pull something upward, you must first push downward, causing the root to be severed and the object to be immediately toppled.

The insubstantial and the substantial should be clearly discriminated. Each single part of the body has both a substantial and an insubstantial aspect at any given time and the body in its entirety also has an insubstantial and a substantial aspect. All the joints of the whole body are to be threaded together without the slightest severance.

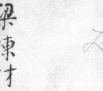

Master T.T. Liang's translation of the T'ai-Chi Ch'uan Classic, signed in Chinese and English and chopped.

Cheng Man-ch'ing's secrets were to read the Classics and give exact explanations. You have to know how to read the old characters because understanding only comes by combining reading, explanation and practice. Cheng was the only teacher who could explain the Classics so well, in so much detail. My other teachers couldn't explain as deeply as Professor Cheng.

☙

Wang Chung-yueh's Classics are "a composition that embodies the contributions of previous scholars."

The Classics say: "There is no stiff adversary who cannot be overthrown." That means if you are tense, I can uproot you—the harder the better. If you are soft, I must reconsider, but no matter how hard you are, I want to uproot you. If someone is really soft, you have to make them stiff. Whoever is softer is the higher rank. Whoever is more firmly rooted knows all the techniques, is more sensitive and is more patient can win. Like Cheng Man-ch'ing, his art is really beautiful. I learned from so many teachers, sometimes I can push them over. In Taiwan, there was a man named Liang Tzu-peng; he was really good. I tried Pushing-Hands with him. He couldn't move me and I couldn't move him. But Professor Cheng knocked him down. He came to challenge Professor Cheng. As soon as they started, just as their hands touched, bang—Professor Cheng knocked him down. This Mr. Liang really wanted to push, so Professor Cheng could push him because he was stiff. Because he was so strong, Professor Cheng could knock him down like a small baby.

The Classics say: "If you pay full attention to your spirit of vitality and ignore your breathing, your striking force will be as strong as pure steel. If you only pay attention to your breathing, your striking force will be inactive and ineffective, and your ch'i will be impeded." After you master breathing, you must forget it. You must do the Solo Form using only the "Yi." What is the Yi? It is mind-intent. You have to know in all the postures what the practical use is. When you know the practical use, you will do the postures differently. Why? If you don't know how to use the postures, they become empty, meaningless. That means you have no intention, no spirit of vitality, no knowledge of how to do it. Gradually you'll forget how to execute the movements correctly. You'll start doing something else. In every posture you must keep the application—same as the Sword, sometimes cutting the wrist, sometimes the leg. Weapons are the same as the Solo Form. You must momentarily stop at the end of each posture. This must be very clear. You continuously move from the beginning to the end of each posture and then pause at the end. The middle is continuously moving, but at the end, you stop. The stop means you use the mind to connect it to the next posture—this is not so easy, this is advanced. At the beginning you have to work to master it. Then there will be no use to think about how to do it; you'll do it naturally. It is like when you go to the bathroom many times a day, daily going there. So many years you know where the bathroom is. Do you ask yourself every time where is the bathroom? No! You never think of it, you just go there. No need to use the mind; you can relax. Otherwise, if you have to use the mind for every action, it will drive you crazy. No need to concentrate your whole mind—relax. This is Yi.

Master Liang lecturing on his ten theorems in Minneapolis, 1985.

A lot of people don't know the Classics. I know the old literature. I learned it when I was young. Then I studied the Classics and asked Professor Cheng for explanations. A lot of young people can't understand the old characters. They have no interest to learn the old writing. I asked Professor Cheng many questions the other students didn't know how to ask. Then he would explain what it really means. No other high-level T'ai-Chi teachers could explain them to me—only Professor Cheng. He knew the old literature and techniques. So you have to stick to the rules; gradually you'll reach a high level. If you don't know the old characters, you won't understand his explanations. The Classics say what to do, Professor Cheng explained and demonstrated how to do it, and combining these two, you get the whole meaning. I learned from Professor Cheng, and then I translated the Classics into English directly from Chinese.

When you practice, you must have your whole body as one unit, not separate. The Classics say: "The entire body should be light and agile and all of its parts connected like a string of pearls. The ch'i should be stimulated, and the spirit of vitality should be retained internally." How can you make your body light and agile? It is not so easy. You have to practice for a long, long time. Year after year, then you will get it. In the beginning

Li Chien-fei, Master Liang's sword teacher, demonstrating the sword form in Taiwan in the late 1950s.

you are very clumsy, stopping and jerky. Gradually you will reach the stage where your whole body is not only light and agile but also connected like a string of pearls. When you push, everything is connected, moving. Not just one part, the whole body will move. Then the ch'i should be stimulated; this is very hard. Gradually, after you have practiced for a long time, inside, the ch'i will start to be stimulated. You stimulate the ch'i when your tan-t'ien goes up and down (with diaphragmatic breathing). Up and down produces heat. After the ch'i becomes hot, it will push the blood to circulate through the whole body. When the ch'i is hot, it turns to steam. Ordinarily the ch'i is a passive, latent power. When you stimulate it though, going from warm to hot, it will circulate. When you practice, the spirit should remain inside, not going out. Even during combat, keep the spirit inside and calm. Internally, I watch you like a cat. I watch you closely to see what is your next move. Otherwise, if your spirit is exposed, your whole body will be tense.

When using a T'ai-Chi kick, you must hold them; make a defect position, then kick. Every posture is that way. Hold them; make it so they can't move. In T'ai-Chi that means a "good opportunity and a superior position." You have to have a chance from your opponent. And you have to have your one good position. You have these two, and then you start to act. If you don't have these two, that means your whole body is in confusion. That means you have to be adjusted by the legs and waist. Did you read that one? If you don't have these two, then you push. That's a blind push. That's no use. So you must get these two. You have to be perfect, in a superior position, then make them in a defect position, then it's easy to push them. That means I can knock you over. If you don't use this principle, whoever is stronger will win. Very few people know this.

Wang Chung-yueh lived about 200 hundred years after Chang San-feng. Chang's classic is short, only a few verses, but Wang's two classics have everything in it. He put together all the details. Just like Confucius, Chang's writing is only a little bit. Afterwards in Mencius' writings, everything in Confucious' teachings is explained in detail.

I'll give you an example. Chang San-feng said: *No deficiency, no excess.* Wang Chung-yueh said: *There should be no excess and no insufficiency. You bend as your opponent stretches out and contract as he contracts.* That means not stretching too much, but just enough. That means when you go back, bend back or shift back, I follow you to push. Then, when you come to me, I bend or go back. If you are hard, yang, I become yin. This is called retreat. You advance, I retreat. That means I'm in a good position. Then, when you are in a defect position, I attack you.

Also, Chang San-feng said: *The insubstantial and the substantial should be clearly discriminated.* Wang Chung-yueh said: *If you keep your weight on one side, you can adapt to all circumstances; if you "double-weight," your actions will be impeded. We often see one who has painstakingly practiced T'ai-Chi for several years but cannot neutralize an attacking energy and is generally subdued by an opponent. This is because he still has not understood the fault of double-weighting. If you want to get rid of this defect, you must know yin and yang.* He gives so much detail! He tells you that if you put the weight on one foot, then you'll get the advantage. If the weight is on two feet, double-weighted, then you are stuck there, no good. I often see years of this pure work, that means you are a hard worker for many years but still cannot neutralize. If you cannot neutralize, you are under the control of others. The reason is double-weighting. You still don't know it. If you want to get rid of this kind of bad habit, you've got to get the yin and yang in coordination. Then you will know how to interpret energy. What is yin and yang in coordination? Yang comes to me; I'm immediately yin. You become yin; I immediately become yang. When these two are in coordination, then you know how to interpret strength. Wang continues to explain: *The fundamental point is to forget yourself and follow others. But most people misunderstand it and sacrifice the near for the far.* What is this? I give up myself and follow your way. See, I only follow you; I have no purpose or intention of my own. Whatever you do, I follow you. You go back, I go forward. You go forward, I go back. You go left, I go left. I always follow what you are doing. Most people don't know this. They go very, very far away. They do something else. That means one mistake takes you 1,000 miles away. So when you practice Pushing-Hands, let your partner push you. If you can avoid it, turn it aside. That's the best way. No resisting. That's not Pushing-Hands' way.

CHAPTER VI

Taoist Meditation, Philosophy & Ch'i-Kung

If you practice reverse breathing, where your tan-t'ien contracts on inhalation and expands on exhalation, you will accumulate ch'i very quickly and your level of martial art will go very high. The only problem is that it takes a toll on the internal organs, so it is not the best for health and longevity. If you practice natural breathing where the tan-t'ien expands on inhalation and contracts on exhalation, the progress of accumulating ch'i is slower but it is the safest, most correct way for health and longevity. Reverse breathing makes the ch'i accumulate too fast and the energy can drive you crazy. Yang Pan-hou practiced reverse breathing and reached a high level, but he died at 54. His father, Yang Lu-chan, practiced natural breathing and reached the highest level and lived to be 73. Yang Chien-hou also practiced natural breathing and reached the same level as his brother Pan-hou, but he lived to be 77.

You need a method for concentration, like counting or breathing or applications, so your mind won't be confused or scattered. Then you can empty it.

You want to exhale longer than inhaling. When exhaling, you want all these dirty things to go out, go out as much as possible. Inhale a little shorter because there is always a little bit of oxygen inside all the time. A lot of meditation teachers told me this. Even the Buddhists do it this way.

Mind-intent equals imagination. Imagination will become reality.

One of the relaxation techniques I learned from the Taoist Monk Yang is to concentrate the mind-intent on the Bubbling-Well point of the substantial foot. I imagine my weight going three feet into the ground. This takes the attention off the legs and lets them relax.

When you breathe with the tan-t'ien, you accumulate ch'i. When the ch'i is full, it rises up the spine to the top of the head, becoming spirit of vitality. To help the spirit rise, you concentrate on the "third eye." If you concentrate on the top of the head, the energy will get stuck at the base of the skull.

If you practice slowly, continuously, effortlessly and without using external muscular force, the ch'i will sink to the tan-t'ien and the blood will circulate through the whole

Master T.T. Liang with, from left, Ray Hayward, Almonzo Lamaroieux, Paul Gallagher, and Twin Cities T'ai-Chi Ch'uan's founding teacher, Jonah Friedman, at Master Liang's basement studio in St. Cloud, Minn., in the summer of 1985.

body without hindrance. Ch'i is an inherent oxygen in the body for stamina and vitality. Ch'i is not breathing or breath; you've had it since you were born, latent in your body. When the ch'i sinks to the tan-t'ien and you exercise, gradually the ch'i will become warm, then hot—so hot it will penetrate into the bone, so hot it will push the blood through the body. When your blood circulates through your entire body, you will enjoy good health. So, after the ch'i sinks, a kind of intrinsic energy will be developed. When you use it, your whole body will be one unit, not just the hand going. If you use the hand to strike out, the energy comes from the bone. If you use the bone, the whole body will be tense, which is not good for health. Also, the hand is not as effective. If the intrinsic energy is developed, when you strike out with the whole body, it is powerful and strong, then you can reach the highest level. So the Classics say: "You have hands everywhere on your body, but it has nothing to do with hands." When you use the energy, it is very fast. The Classics say: "Withdraw means attack." That means the two actions are one. The two movements are one, so it looks slow, but it is really faster and to the point.

What does it matter who my teacher is? Everyone is my teacher, that's all. I don't want to be a teacher myself; everybody is my teacher. In reality, who is more free in America?

The student—the teacher really suffers. You go to class, the teacher has to stand up in front and the students just sit down and ask questions.

Sometimes it takes an extraordinary situation to bring out our hidden energy. Like Yang Pan-hou—after he accidentally killed his daughter in a training session, he was seen to levitate. It took great grief and anger to make him release his power. He had the power all the time, but he didn't know how to let it out. But his father, Yang Lu-chan, learned how to release it anytime. The only way is constant practice.

From constant practice, the ch'i will become so hot that it will evaporate and permeate the bones to become marrow. When the bones are full they will become strong and heavy. This is what is meant by "iron bars wrapped in cotton."

In the Taoist theory of changing ching to ch'i and ch'i to shen, not one of these may be lacking. Ching is sperm. The sperm must be full and should be kept calm by avoiding stimulating foods and not having too many emissions. When the ching is full, it is evaporated by breathing with the tan-t'ien. The ching mixes with breath to make ch'i. The ch'i is stimulated by regular, relaxed and rhythmical exercise using tan-t'ien breathing. When the ch'i is stimulated enough—this takes time—it produces heat. This hot ch'i evaporates into shen, or spirit of vitality. A byproduct of this heat is that some of the evaporating ch'i permeates the bones, becoming marrow that makes the bones heavier and stronger. A sign of full spirit of vitality is penetrating, sparkling eyes. The eyes are sharp and can see for a great distance.

The Taoist I studied with (his name was Yang, but not related to the Yang family) studied with Yang Pan-hou. His postures were low and slow. He taught me to concentrate the energy into the Bubbling-Well point. When all your energy is concentrated there, your whole body is relaxed and your blood can circulate everywhere in your body. The technique is to use our mind-intent to direct your energy there.

You can measure spirit of vitality by the brightness of the eyes.

Don't think of the future or the past, only the present.

Master Liang relaxing at home in Tampa, Fla., 1989.

Try to make it (T'ai-Chi) correct; otherwise, if a pattern is formed, it will be hard to change it.

In the Tao Te Ching it says: "From nothing to something, from something to nothing." That means when you are born, there is nothing in your mind. Then you have to learn as much as possible about everything. Once you learn everything, you must try to empty your mind; otherwise all these things will drive you crazy.

Ch'i-Kung is a quick way to develop ch'i, but it can wear out the body. Ch'i-Kung artificially stimulates the ch'i while T'ai-Chi naturally develops ch'i at a rate that is safe and healthy for the body.

The secret to sinking all the weight and concentrating it in the Bubbling-Well point is that, when you step forward in the forms, your foot is empty and your leg is relaxed. When you shift the weight, you must still try to keep that empty (relaxed) feeling. Then the weight can sink and you can have free circulation everywhere.

You must learn to yield. That way, in times of emergency, you will know how to deal with people.

I can tell a person's nature by how they do their postures—whether they are smooth, jerky, slow or hasty. You must learn to yield, not argue. Today you may be right, but tomorrow you may be wrong. Sometimes everyone thinks something is right, then later it is wrong. Like Hitler—at one time the people worshipped him. Who knows, some day he might come back!

When you breathe with your stomach, you not only breathe with the front (tan-t'ien) but you also expand the sides and the back as well. This stimulates the kidneys and increases breath capacity.

Master Liang said Cheng Man-ch'ing received a premonition about his death. So he worked night and day to finish his commentary on the Tao Te Ching. Soon after it was completed, Cheng died. Master Liang said Cheng should have heeded the warning, relaxed, just practiced T'ai-Chi and not worked so hard, then he could have lived longer. Liang said because of Cheng's ego, he had to finish the book.

Master Liang knows how concentrated or how deep in meditation the student is while doing the Form by how much they blink their eyes. Less blinking means a calm mind, more, an active mind.

Master Liang said that to become a disciple, you have to know all the forms and you have to change your temperament.

To practice the Form by mind-intent is to use and train the attention. Keep the shen inside, but observe all. In the Two-Person Form, watch your partner. Master Liang demonstrated attention by describing my face and body movement without looking at me. His expression was relaxed.

First, you do the postures by counting them out. Then you just follow your breath. Then you just use your mind. The highest is emptiness.

You still must circulate energy with your mind while doing postures, until everything is perfected. Then you can empty the mind.

If you practice T'ai-Chi for a long time, it should change your temperament.

If you sweat a little bit, it is okay—this cleans the pores. If you sweat too much, you must replenish the liquid because the energy comes from the internal organs.

You must presume that you have an opponent. Imagine you push them far, far away.

You must forget your breath and empty your mind. You must feel the air at all times. If you don't feel anything, that is wasted practice. You must feel some resistance. Then your ch'i will circulate and your hands will swell and tingle.

Master Liang said it was Cheng Man-ch'ing who said, "The hands must embrace the 8-Trigrams and the feet must step on the 5-Elements." When his students asked what it means, Cheng said, "Even if I explain it to you, you still won't understand."

I am teaching you to yield. I try to intimidate you. If you laugh, you win. If you get angry, I win.

The Taoist Yang would circulate his ch'i to the Bubbling-Well point in seated and standing meditation. He was the only one I met who reached the level of being truly sunken. If he stood on one leg, you could feel his leg still soft. He could also root my push standing on one leg.

We have two ways of breathing—before-heaven and after-heaven breathing. I prefer, when your energy goes out, you breathe out, not holding the breath while you push. Suppose someone counters you; your internal organs will be hurt. You should breathe out even if someone knocks you down; if your lungs are empty, you won't be hurt.

The theory of T'ai-Chi is based entirely on the Taoist way—Lao-tzu's way.

❧

If someone wants to rob you, give them your money. If they want to kill you, do you think you still yield? No!

❧

Mental Accomplishment in T'ai-Chi means to change your temperament, to change your nature. When practice Pushing-Hands, you must know how to yield, not to be aggressive.

❧

The way of immortality starts at age 70. At this time you have to rid yourself of fame, wealth and desire because they are all dirt. They have nothing to do with you. At this age you really think about the way of immortality. You will really want to be immortal.

❧

Don't be concerned with being as good as Yang Lu-ch'an, it will only hold you back. Just practice.

Many classes started with Master Liang sorting his books and notes on the forms and lessons that he was teaching.

❧

You know what alchemy is? One way is to change metal into gold, the other is to make you live longer.

❧

You practiced T'ai-Chi and changed your temperament. Good boy!

❧

A lot of things you have to learn to be my disciple, such as how to yield—everything, even if somebody says something bad to you. Learn how to yield. Like when that man said something wrong about you. Forget it.

The qualifications of a disciple: First of all, they must know all of my art—the forms, the weapons, the Classics—to my satisfaction. That is the first. Second, I look to see if they are a good person. The most important is personality. Character is very important. You must not be aggressive. Try to yield, not to gain. Don't argue. Don't be angry. This is very hard.

So far, now that you are teaching T'ai-Chi for a living, you find out it's not so easy. No matter what happens, you must know how to deal with it, how to face it.

When a teacher wants to hand down their art, they must find out if their student is really good. Otherwise the teacher's time and effort are wasted. I want my students to be better than I am. If they aren't better, that means my art is terrible—cannot be handed down to anybody. This exercise, T'ai-Chi, is for everybody, whole world exercise.

If someone comes to challenge me, I don't fight. I say, you are the best, please be my teacher. Then trouble is neutralized.

Don't say you don't know it (a form) if you do. It's good you don't want to show off. The correct way to be truthful and humble is to say you know a little bit. If you say you don't know, that means you're a big liar. Don't cheat your teacher. That's incorrect.

Mental Accomplishment means to change a person's temperament or nature. A human's nature is to have a hot temper, quick to fight. If you practice T'ai-Chi, gradually a hot temper will be changed into a mild one. A complete change comes so that you won't have trouble in your life. Otherwise, with a hot temper, you will have trouble.

If you don't know something, or only know it halfway or not at all, just say, "I don't know." This saves ch'i (breath) and keeps you relaxed and out of trouble.

(To my mother at a dinner held for Master Liang.) I want to know about him as a little boy. Was he a good boy or a bad boy? Did he obey you? I want to know everything.

Everything is different. Everything changes, so adapt to the circumstances.

There is only one thing better than T'ai-Chi to change your temperament—marriage. This is quite true. This automatically trains you. You have no choice.

These two masters (Paul Abdella and I) come to bug me and mug me.

Ray Hayward, left, and Paul Abdella, right, taking Master Liang to the airport when he left Minnesota in 1988.

CHAPTER VII

CHENG MAN-CH'ING

Master Liang had 15 different teachers of T'ai-Chi Ch'uan. He said that Cheng Man-ch'ing was the best and that he adopted Cheng's way of T'ai-Chi.

There are many techniques of counterattack. All these things, these techniques, I learned from Cheng Man-ch'ing, which were handed down to him from his teachers, Yang Cheng-fu and Chang Ch'ing-ling. All these techniques he learned belonged to the Yang family.

Master Liang is the Chief Disciple of Cheng Man-ch'ing and one of his first students. Liang said that at the time he first started learning from Cheng, he met two of Cheng's students from the mainland. Liang said both had high levels, but he didn't know what became of them.

Professor Cheng's masterpiece technique was to circle you out of the way, off-balance you, then push you suddenly.

When Cheng would fight with someone who threw a lot of punches, he would remain calm and wait for the real one, then neutralize and counter. Cheng would stand in Retreat to Ride Tiger and wait and tempt the opponent to kick, and then he would catch their kick and push. He protected his groin by turning in the toes of his front foot.

In creating his Short Form, Cheng Man-ch'ing deleted the postures from the Long Form that he felt were Shao-Lin style.

Besides Pushing-Hands, Professor Cheng practiced an exercise called "knock the tofu." This exercise should be practiced for ten years. We don't have such patience. With a chopstick you stand there, put tofu on a dish and gesture at it. Not touching it; ch'i going out to it. First do ten minutes a day, gradually increase to one hour. Don't put energy on it, use ch'i. After you are done practicing, eat the tofu. After a certain time, when you eat it, the tofu becomes hard, that means you got something. From the body, to the hand, to the cake, ch'i goes to the tofu. Not touch it, but it goes to it. So Cheng's hand was very soft, but when he touched you, you would be bruised. His hand was like a lady, no veins protruding. We call this beauty hand. It was very soft externally, like nothing, but internally, very strong.

Professor Cheng Man-ch'ing with some of his students and their wives in Taiwan, early 1960s.

Cheng Man-ch'ing said that when practicing alone, presume you have an opponent in front of you. When facing an opponent, imagine you are practicing alone.

When Professor Cheng would grab me, the next day I would have five small bruises from his fingertips. After Pushing-Hands with him, my body would have bruises all over. That is because his energy was so sharp.

During World War II, Cheng Man-ch'ing was an official and fled to Chun-King, where he met Chang Ch'ing-ling. Chang Ch'ing-ling learned from Yang Chien-hou, but was recorded as Yang Cheng-fu's disciple. When Cheng met Chang, they tried some Pushing-Hands. Chang Ch'ing-ling knocked Cheng down like a small baby. Then Cheng studied with Chang. Most of the Pushing-Hands techniques come from Chang. When Cheng Man-ch'ing fled to Taiwan, Chang stayed on the mainland. Cheng wrote to Chang Ch'ing-ling and got so much information about the Classics. When the Iron Curtain fell, they stopped writing. Cheng took a lot of that information and put it into his "Thirteen Chapters."

One time Professor Cheng was in trouble in the mainland. He defeated some foreign soldiers in a public match. As he was leaving, one master patted him on the back to congratulate him. The next day, Professor Cheng was sick, could not get out of bed. Cheng's friend knew of a master and asked him to come and cure him. The master cured him and told him that now that Professor Cheng was famous, he shouldn't be proud.

Cheng Man-ch'ing had a match with a Pa-Kua master named Liu. Cheng stood in the middle and followed him around, always on guard. As soon as Liu closed in to attack, Cheng found a defect and knocked him down. T'ai-Chi is called the center, and that is where we fight from. Cheng had equilibrium; even if he was hit, he couldn't be knocked down. He was so firmly rooted, his body was so soft, he could neutralize fast.

Master Liang said Cheng Man-ch'ing truly received the techniques of T'ai-Chi. Cheng got all the Classics and techniques from Yang Cheng-fu and Chang Ch'ing-ling. Because Professor Cheng was a literary scholar, he was able to read the Classics and explain them. His body was soft, but his energy was sharp.

When Master Liang first went to the park to learn from Cheng Man-ch'ing, he was sick with cirrhosis of the liver. Cheng, being a Chinese doctor, felt Liang's pulses and then walked away. Liang asked what he found, but Cheng wouldn't answer. Later, a student said Cheng told him Master Liang would live two years at most. When Liang heard this, he made up his mind to practice diligently. Cheng Man-ch'ing lived to age 74. Master Liang lived to 102.

Vertical circling Pushing-Hands is the old style. After Cheng Man-ch'ing learned from Chang Ch'ing-ling, he made it horizontal. The four moves are clearly distinguished and scientific. The old way has the four moves in it, but they are hard to see.

Cheng Man-ch'ing once had a job teaching T'ai-Chi to the captains of the Huang-P'u Military Academy. After six months, some of the men had doubts about Cheng's ability because he was short and slight and never sparred with anybody. Word got around to the director, who was a Shao-Lin expert, so he decided to test Cheng. They went to a secluded courtyard to try some techniques. After half an hour they came out with the director thoroughly convinced. For half an hour he tried to attack Cheng, but couldn't touch him. Cheng hadn't even tried to counterattack.

One time Master Liang was at Cheng Man-ch'ing's house for class. During a break he sat on the couch next to Cheng. Cheng hit Liang with his hip and knocked him sprawling off the couch. Cheng looked down at him and said, "The energy can be issued from anywhere. Everywhere has the potential for attack."

꙰

At the second level of T'ai-Chi, you don't need to neutralize. When your opponent is about to push, you can feel some kind of stir or tension. Then you push first, taking advantage of their yang. You must have a root and develop sharp intrinsic energy. My teacher, Cheng Man-ch'ing, reached this level. When the energy is developed, it is used for everything, like pushing or using the spear or sword.

꙰

Master Liang said Cheng Man-ch'ing told him Step Back to Repulse the Monkey is the most important posture. He also said Roll-Back is the most important technique.

꙰

When Cheng Man-ch'ing was accepting public challenges, a famous master named Tu Hsin-wu came for a friendly match. When they joined, Cheng put his hands on Tu's body, ready to push. Like lightening, Tu put his foot on Cheng's chest. Neither moved, because both were waiting for any action to issue their energy—Cheng through his hand, Tu through his foot. The match ended in a draw.

꙰

Master Liang said Cheng Man-ch'ing was the best because his hands and body were so soft that you couldn't detect what he was going to do. He gave you no chance to prepare yourself.

꙰

Cheng Man-ch'ing learned from the Yang family. In his whole life he never learned hard-style, only soft-style. That he was able to reach such a high level is not so easy—it's really something.

꙰

Cheng Man-ch'ing would explain the Classics one by one. If you follow his explanation, gradually you'll get it. That's the secret. All the T'ai-Chi Classics explained, then practiced. You see Professor Cheng; everything he did was according to the Classics. He practiced and showed examples.

꙰

I called Cheng Man-ch'ing Shih-fu after I passed a discipleship ceremony, like I did with you. I called him that after we passed the ceremony. At my ceremony, he gave me some words of advice and told me about the founder. No matter whether my teacher is bad or good, I must serve him. Life and death are in the hands of God. I never dreamed Professor Cheng would die before me. His body was so strong, never sick. I am one year older than he—I am Ox year; he was Tiger.

Cheng Man-ch'ing told me do the Solo Form like swimming in the air. Because when you swim in the water, the water resists you, same with the air. The water resists you, you can feel it. If you use the air, your blood will circulate. So first, you feel the air with your hands, then when you shift forward, you feel it with your chest. Even when doing the kicks you feel it, your feet are so heavy. That's the best way. Nobody, I think, does T'ai-Chi that way. They just go. But, if you feel something on your hands, energy will move. Otherwise you'll feel nothing, which means that you have no intrinsic energy. Professor Cheng told me that and many other valuable things. For instance, Roll-Back and how to use it; he said that if you know how to use it in Pushing-Hands, that means you got half of the active part of the art.

Master Liang told this story many times; in Taiwan, he was scheduled to give a public demonstration of T'ai-Chi Ch'uan. Liang asked his teacher, Professor Cheng Man-ch'ing, to come to the demo, as a sort of blessing upon what Liang was doing. Professor Cheng asked, "Are you going to do the Long Form?" Liang answered, "Yes." Cheng asked, "Are you going to do T'ai-Chi to music?" Liang answered, "Yes." Cheng asked, "Are you going to demonstrate San-Shou?" Liang answered, "Yes." Professor Cheng then told Master Liang, "This is not my way. You spoiled my art. I won't go."

Master Liang gave the demonstration at the appointed day, and just as he walked out on to stage, he saw Professor Cheng sitting in the audience in the front row. After the demo, Cheng walked over to Liang and said, "Very good." Master Liang took these words, and the Professor's attendance, as the blessing from his teacher and then went on to teach a more complete, old style T'ai-Chi curriculum.

Master Liang was in the first group of Professor Cheng's students to learn the T'ai-Chi sword. Cheng taught them to hold the sword in a relaxed, alive grip, based on the grip of a calligraphy brush. Some of Liang's classmates had also studied Shao-Lin and one asked the Professor how such a loose, relaxed grip could be useful. Cheng told the student to hit his sword as hard as he can and try to knock the sword out of the Professor's grip. The student chopped down on Cheng's sword, but it just circled around and stopped next to his head. Then Cheng told the student to hold the sword as hard as he could. He hit the student's sword with a short chop, and the student's sword popped out of his hand.

CHAPTER VIII

THE YANG FAMILY AND SOME OF THEIR DISCIPLES

First, Yang Lu-ch'an learned Shao-Lin and reached a high level in this art. Then he heard of T'ai-Chi and went to the Chen village. The Chens never taught outsiders, only relatives. How could Yang learn? From Peking, he traveled to Chen Chia Kou because he wanted to learn, but they wouldn't accept him. So he played mute and became a servant, sweeping floors, everything. Chen Chang-hsing accepted him to be a servant there. Every time Chen would call his students—his relatives—to practice, Yang would secretly peek outside and watch them. He would remember and gradually learn more of the techniques. One day he was watching them learn a new technique. He tried to imitate it, but couldn't understand it. Another day while watching, Chen gave an explanation of the technique and Yang let out a shout on the roof. Chen ran up expecting to catch a robber. When he saw it was Yang, he said, "You can't speak, but we heard a shout." Chen continued, "If you like T'ai-Chi, let me see your technique and fight with my student." Yang easily defeated the student and from then on was accepted as a student. He worked hard and after a while learned everything.

Afterward, a banquet was given for Yang before he left to return to his home village. Chen told all his relatives gathered there, "I wanted to give my art to all of you, but you didn't get it. This man, Yang, I didn't want to show, but he got it all." Yang returned to Peking and started teaching in the palace. Tung Hai-ch'uan, a eunuch, was the emperor's bodyguard and very powerful in the palace. Yang Lu-ch'an was teaching T'ai-Chi to the royal family. At the time, Yang didn't know too many officials and had limited political power. Tung would send the young eunuchs to make trouble for Yang. Tung was very famous for the Pa-Kua Chang style, so Yang had to be careful. If he knocked Tung down, not only would he lose his job but he also might get murdered. If Tung defeated Yang, Yang would lose his job. If Tung defeated him, Yang would lose face, so this was a difficult position. One day Tung had his servant send the palace dogs to attack Yang. Yang just stood there as the dogs bit his legs. The next day the dogs wouldn't eat. Something was wrong. When the servants opened the dogs' mouths, their teeth were broken! Yang just issued energy into his legs and they were hard as steel.

There are a lot of stories of how they tried to torture Yang, but they couldn't succeed. One day Yang and Tung met face to face and decided to see who was superior. This is quite interesting because both had the light technique. As soon as you touched them, they could jump and fly up to the roof. So, when one would go up, the other would follow. Yang was using his T'ai-Chi and Tung was using Pa-Kua. Yang had to hold back and Tung tried his best to knock Yang down, but he couldn't do it. Yang couldn't knock Tung down because of politics, but he wouldn't allow himself to be knocked down. Yang only used his neutralizing and escaping techniques. The match ended in a draw and they became friends.

January 23, 2000, Students and disciples at Master Liang's 100th birthday party in Andover, NJ. From left are James Postiglione, Ana Ortiz de Montellano, Ray Hayward, Paul Abdella, Diane Cannon, Joey Carroll, Paul Gallagher, J. Richard Roy, Rob Zilin, Ariel Germanton and Bryan Davis.

One way to practice is for two people to place a staff on each other's tan-t'ien and then shift back and forth, alternating pushing and neutralizing. Yang Cheng-fu would let his students punch him in the stomach. Yang would absorb the whole fist, holding their fist with his stomach muscles. When they tried to pull their hand out, Yang would release his energy and knock them out.

I saw Yang Cheng-fu when I was in high school in Peking. At that time I liked to practice Shao-Lin. After I learned from Cheng Man-ch'ing, I heard all the stories of Yang's achievements.

Yang Cheng-fu went to Shanghai, but was forced to leave because his students knocked down Wu Chien-ch'uan's students. A Wu stylist, Chu Ming-i was a minister there and threatened to make trouble for Yang. Yang was invited by eight people to go to Canton to teach them privately. One man, a florist named Mr. Huang Tzu-chen, was one of the eight. I learned the Long Form from him in New York City. He told me that Canton was bad for Yang because it was damp there. Yang's legs swelled with gout and he had to teach from his bed. He died there.

Master Liang painted this portrait of T'ai-Chi Ch'uan founder, Chang San-feng, in 1980.

Chang Ch'ing-ling was a disciple of Yang Chien-hou, but is recorded as Yang Cheng-fu's disciple. The Chang family were farmers and fur merchants. Chang would go out into the field and stand on two rocks. He would mobilize his ch'i and push the rocks into the ground with his rooting power. Chang's body was so soft and flexible. He would practice Brush Knee and Twist Step, left and right styles, going through a hollow log. Chang was not an ordinary practitioner. He also practiced the Solo Form under a table.

Yang Lu-chan reached the highest level of T'ai-Chi. When you touched his body, he would relax, then issue energy. You couldn't see his neutralization. His issuing energy was so sharp that the opponent would be knocked out or thrown over or both. Wherever you touched, he would receive your energy and then knock you down. Even from behind, he could feel the pressure of the air in front of a fist coming at him. He could defend himself from behind. This level is called "Automatic Receiving."

When I was young, I saw Yang Cheng-fu practicing with his students in the park. They had nets strung in trees and Yang would do Pushing-Hands with them. He would call out which net he intended to send them into and, defend as they might, they would end up in the net indicated. They would be lifted up and thrown into the net.

I learned from Li Shou-ch'ien in Taiwan for nine years. He was one of only a few disciples of Yang Shao-hou. Li's postures were done at medium speed with some energy. His postures were small frame. He lived to be about 91 or 93. His temperament was aggressive, which was one reason he could stand the severe training of Yang Shao-hou. In Taiwan, he constantly criticized Shao-Lin people. Only after he was old did the Shao-Lin people come to challenge him. No one dared try him in his prime. He reached a high level of T'ai-Chi. One important teaching of Yang Shao-hou I got through Li is to always look forward to a presumed opponent. Always feel the presence of someone. Like in Brush Knee or Repulse Monkey, don't look back at the circling hand, only turn to the corner, which is far enough to circle the hand while still looking in the direction of the presumed opponent.

When Yang Chien-hou would go to bed at night, he would practice using his mind to circulate the ch'i. As the ch'i would circulate, his body would shake and tremble. When the ch'i went through his joints, they would expand and crack loudly. A servant heard the noises through the door.

CHAPTER IX

STORIES OF MASTER T.T. LIANG

Master Liang's "baby name" was Bao-Hsiang. His school name was Chuan-Wu. And the name he gave himself was Tung-Tsai, meaning "important material" or the "highest beam in a house."

Four-year-old Liang, left, with his father, Ming-ru, and sister Bao-mei in Imperial China.

⌘

In the summer of 1979, Master Liang invited Dr. Leung Kay-chi, a Martial Arts expert who was visiting the United States, to come to Boston to teach me Hsing-Yi and Pa-Kua. The first night Dr. Leung arrived, Master Liang asked him to give us a demonstration. Dr. Leung performed the 12-Animals Linking Form of Hsing-Yi, which I later learned was one of his specialties. The form was incredible. Dr. Leung was running across the room stamping, punching and turning, all with amazing speed and power. I had never, in all my previous experience, seen anything like it. When he was done, Dr. Leung walked around to compose himself. I looked at Master Liang and he looked at me. I, 19 at the time, said with excitement, "Wow, that was great!" Master Liang, 79 at the time, said calmly, "Hard-style."

⌘

When Master Liang first moved to St. Cloud, Minn., there was a T'ai-Chi instructor teaching in Minneapolis, an American, whom we'll call Harry. Some of Harry's students made the one-and-a-half-hour journey to Master Liang's house for lessons. The students came back and told Harry that Liang was a true master and that his level was higher. Harry decided to go up and see who was better. Harry brought Liang some gifts and then said he wanted to see who would rank higher. Liang said there was no need to try Pushing-Hands or free-fighting. Liang said he'd just test Harry's root, his rooting ability. Liang told Harry to stand in front of a mattress against the wall and try to root against his push. If Harry could resist, Liang would retire and hand over all his students to him. Liang pushed, and Harry went sprawling into the mattress. A second and third time, Liang pushed and Harry couldn't root. Harry asked, could Liang root his push? So he pushed and Liang resisted each attempt. Harry left. Liang was 83 at the time. Three students witnessed this encounter.

Later on, one of Harry's students asked what happened when he met Master Liang. Harry said Liang was quite strong and pushed him into the mattresses. But, Harry added, Liang didn't use ch'i, he used external muscular force. That student went back to Liang and told him that Harry said Liang pushed him over but that he had used external muscular force.

Master Liang smiled and said, "Yes, and he couldn't even neutralize that."

Master Liang's wife, Mrs. Liang Jou Shu-wen, told me the following story, with Master Liang sitting next to her laughing and nodding. One time, during supper, Mrs. Liang noticed that around Master Liang's wrist, there were black dots. She started to criticize him, saying he should take better care when practicing calligraphy. He should not be getting ink all over himself. Liang defended himself saying he never spilled any ink. She said, "No, you have been very messy. Look, you even have ink on both wrists." Master Liang looked at his wrists and saw little black spots and circles, which hurt when he touched them. He then went to a mirror, lifted his shirt, and saw big black and blue marks on his chest and ribs. He went back to Mrs. Liang and told her it was not ink, it was bruises from Professor Cheng's fingertips and palms, after practicing Pushing-Hands with him. His wrists were bruised from Cheng's pulls, and his body was bruised from his pushes, so sharp was Professor Cheng's short energy techniques (Da-Chin).

Master Liang was the highest ranking officer in the Taiwanese Customs Service. He is in the front row, center.

MARRIAGE PHOTO OF
PETITIONER TUNG TSAI LIANG
(梁棟材) AND BENEFICIARY
SHU WEN CHOW LIANG
(梁周淑雯) TAKEN
IN TIENTSIN, CHINA
OCT. 27TH 1942

Master Liang was quite the wordsmith and really enjoyed all aspects of learning English, especially slang. In his 80s, he attended an English literature class, then would read Dickens to us in class. He actually read the dictionary and kept us spellbound with his command of vocabulary. He would leave professors silent with questions like, what is the difference between stealing and robbing? (In robbing the victim is present.) Here are some anecdotes I'd like to share.

At a grocery store, the cashier took Master Liang's money, then pushed his bag of groceries toward him and said, "There you go." Liang replied, "Where I go?"

Once I swore in class and he said, "Did you expect the cur to spit ivory from his mouth?"

While talking about being relaxed, Master Liang told us a Chinese saying: "When the tiger walks down the street, even the dog can harass him," meaning that when you are out of your environment, you will experience tension and worry.

One time I asked to borrow one of Master Liang's old T'ai-Chi books. I promised to return it and when he reluctantly handed it over, after much pleading on my part, he said, "Do you know what just happened?" I replied, somewhat perplexed, "I borrowed your book?" He said, "No, I just hit the dog with a meat dumpling," meaning that he thought he'd never get his book back.

Master Liang once asked us what the difference was between committed and involved. Then he said, "It's like ham and eggs. The chicken is involved, but the pig is committed!"

Master Liang would caution us about putting flowery or extraneous movements into our postures. One time he asked if we knew the definition of superfluous. He said, "Superfluous means to pull your pants down and fart."

Master T.T. Liang at the airport with his wife, Mrs. Liang Jou Shu-wen, second from right, before his departure to the United States in 1964. Tao Ping-siang is directly left of Liang.

When I was first studying with Master Liang in Boston, he mentioned many times about "the masterpiece." The masterpiece, he said, was the one technique the master didn't teach to his students in case any decided to challenge him. The teacher kept this technique as a kind of insurance. He told us that Cheng Man-ch'ing taught him his masterpiece, and Liang said he had one of his own.

When Master Liang decided to move to Minnesota, he gave the students about six months notice so we could finish whatever we were studying at the time. I told him that he hadn't taught me his masterpiece yet; he said he'd show me later. Every time I asked him, he put me off by saying, "I'll show you later." A few months passed and I became nervous. What if he left and I didn't get his secret technique? I was planning to stay in Boston at the time.

About a month before Liang moved, he asked me if there was anything I wanted to learn from him. I said I needed his masterpiece. He said, "All right." He told me, "My masterpiece is this: I know how to change people's temperaments. I know how to make 1,000 friends without making one enemy. All my students are my friends. Do you see any of them who want to hurt me?" He went on to mention some students by name and gave examples of how they had changed. He said, as far as martial arts techniques, he had taught them all, even his secrets, in the classes.

I felt cheated for a long time until the realization hit me—he had given me his masterpiece.

AFTERWORD

I hope this exposure of the teachings of Master T.T. Liang will help the reader in his or her own practice of the art of T'ai-Chi Ch'uan. T'ai-Chi is so vast that it is beyond any one person's or style's definition, and yet, it is such an intimate art that it is the sole possession of the practitioner.

T'ai-Chi Ch'uan is a living gift that grows as it is shared. So, let me share with the reader a truth I have learned in my many years of practicing and studying this art. T'ai-Chi is a tool—a tool that can be used to achieve almost anything. Some have achieved health from sickness—others, strength from weakness—and for some, spiritual awakening from material slumber. T'ai-Chi is a neutral tool that is untainted by anyone's use of it. Whether it is put to good purposes or bad purposes, T'ai-Chi remains, as always, a gift from Nature. Let us use it well.

Ray Hayward brought his son, Alex Hayward, to see Master Liang in his basement studio in St. Cloud, Minn., 1988.

APPENDIX A

Ray Hayward's Answers to a Questionnaire on the Occasion of Master Liang's 100th Birthday, January, 2000

Q When and where did you study with Master Liang?
A 1977 to the present at the following locations: Boston; St. Cloud, Minn.; Tampa, Fla.; Los Angeles; St. Paul, Minn.; and Andover, N.J.

Q Describe his studio.
A I studied in four different studios so I will describe some common qualities. There were mattresses on the wall for Pushing-Hands practice, weapons and weapons racks, calligraphy on the walls and the combined smells of incense, Tiger Balm and food. Except for his house, Master Liang gave me keys to all of the studios and I felt they were sacred practice halls, imbued with the Master's energy, whether he was present or not.

Q Describe his teaching style.
A Studying with Master Liang was an experience that was unique and beyond compare. He had so many teaching methods and techniques that it was like studying with Yoda, Lao-Tse, Don Juan Matus, Bilbo Baggins, Bob Hope, Blind Master Po, Andrew Dice Clay, Yang Lu-chan and the Buddha all wrapped up into one person.

No one, and I repeat no one, knew Professor Cheng Man-ch'ing as well or as deeply as Master Liang. Professor Cheng was the consummate Confucian—very concerned with rank, status, hierarchy and lineage. Cheng bestowed upon Master Liang the rank of Da Hsih-Hsiung (Big Older Brother), which showed that Master Liang was Cheng's successor and had crossed a line of intimacy that no student before or after has ever achieved. Master Liang was Cheng's assistant, translator,

Master Liang and Ray Hayward, 1984.

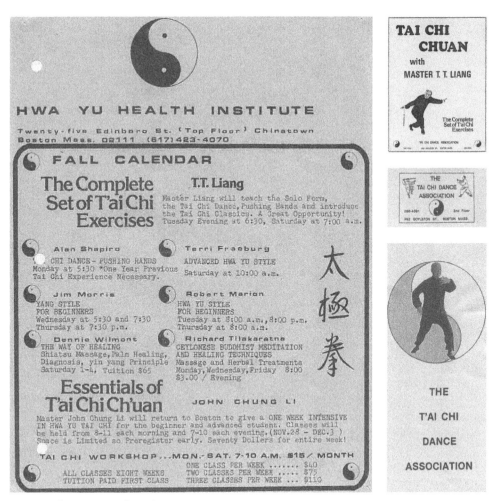

Various advertisements from the Boston years.

co-author and confidant. When Master Liang passed Cheng's teachings to us, it was as if the professor was just in the other room.

Master Liang's knowledge of Chinese history, literature and language, as well as British and American history, literature and language, offered many opportunities to draw parallels and make connections for his Western students. Master Liang used direct and indirect teaching methods, commands, intimidations, and used the "old man" or "dear old grandfather" persona to the fullest advantage.

For me personally, I only wanted to study Martial Arts. Master Liang introduced me to more concepts, principles and methods than any other teacher I have ever had. Only later in my studies did I find out what a great teacher of healing, meditation, philosophy and life he was.

Above all, time has shown that Master Liang's teachings are multi-leveled. Some of his lessons are like ripe fruit, ready to eat and be digested. Others are like a tree or plant

Ray Hayward with Mrs. Liang Jou Shu-wen in St. Cloud, Minn., 1984.

that still needs time to bear fruit. And I'm recently discovering his lessons that were planted in my heart like seeds and are just starting to sprout.

To sum up: although Master Liang could and did use explanations, he also had an uncanny ability to teach through example, which reminds me of a quote from the *Tao Te Ching*: "Teaching without words is understood by the very few."

Q How many other students were in class?
A Group classes were anywhere from 8 to 15. Private classes were usually just me or one or two others.

Q How long did you study with Master Liang?
A July 29, 1977, to the present. I always learn from him—every time I'm in his presence.

Q Describe a typical class.
A Depending upon the subject, we would do five warm-ups, two Ch'i-Kungs and one round of the Long Form. Then Master Liang would get out his notes and materials and he would begin correcting, teaching and reviewing.

In private classes, he was my partner for all the two-person training (a touch is worth a thousand words). We always took a tea break in the middle, and here is where the old master would talk, answer questions, and tell stories and history that would hold us spellbound. Then he would look up at the clock and say, "Oh, I've taken so much of your class time talking about rubbish, so we will go over time."

Q Please recount a story that has lasting memory for you.

A At one point during my relationship with Master Liang I had gone from outsider to insider, from student to assistant, from superficial to intimate. One time, after I had made some mistakes, which I won't discuss here, Master Liang scolded me, saying, "You have disappointed me." I felt the very depth of shame at that moment. Then he said something that shocked me. He said, "But I know I've disappointed you too. What did you expect? Now we can go on." As I grow older, this has been the definition of a functioning student-teacher relationship for me.

Q What is his distinctive contribution to T'ai-Chi?

A Master Liang made the bridges between East and West, Chinese and English, old age and youth, sickness and health, mystery and attainment, and past, present and future.

Q What T'ai-Chi lesson has stuck with you?

A Growing up in the Boston area, it seemed everyone had a scam or a con. When people would ask Master Liang for advice on a physical problem, a worry or concern, or some trouble in their personal life, he always told them, "Try to relax it." I used to think that that was his scam answer to get people to stop bugging him, myself included. I realize now that it wasn't a scam, it was simply that he had distilled the essences of T'ai-Chi, meditation, religion, philosophy and healing into one useful sentence.

Q How would you describe Master Liang?

A I can only describe Master Liang from my personal view and understanding and experience. Master Liang is my teacher, my father, my hero and my inspiration. He not only taught me T'ai-Chi, but he also taught me how to learn, how to teach and how to live life. He introduced me to the friends I have to this day and the lessons I know and give to others. He has truly touched every aspect of my life.

In India there is a saying, "You can have many teachers in this life, but you can only have one master." I have had many teachers in Martial Arts, meditation, religion and healing. Liang Tung-Tsai is my Master.

Q What forms did you learn from Master Liang?

A Besides the Complete Yang Style system of T'ai-Chi Ch'uan, I learned two forms and 25 knockdown techniques from 8-Step Praying Mantis. I also learned Shao-Lin Ch'in-Na and various solo and two-person weapon routines. Master Liang introduced me to other teachers to learn such styles as: Hsing-Yi, Pa-Kua, 7-Star Praying Mantis, Northern Shao-Lin and Eagle Claw. When I met a teacher of Liu Ho Pa Fa and I-Ch'uan, Master Liang said these were excellent styles and encouraged me to pursue them.

Q *Do you remember the use of music or chants in class?*
A Master Liang used exact counts for doing the postures and forms. He felt this kept everyone uniform for demonstrations. He also said, "When the form becomes consistent, the mind will relax." For the two-person routines, the count let you know when to attack and when to defend. Only after mastering the counts did he encourage us to not use the music and rely on internal timing.

Q *Describe the set of warm-up exercises and stretches you did with Master Liang.*
A Master Liang only taught five warm-ups and two Ch'i-Kung exercises.
   The five warm-ups are:
      1. Forward arm swings,
      2. Rub the kidneys 49 times,
      3. Horizontal arm swings,
      4. Waist rotation,
      5. Toe raises and Push the Sky
   The Ch'i-Kungs are:
      1. Walking Du-Na,
      2. "Cross Hands"

Master Liang told us to stretch as much as possible, but he didn't show us any specific methods. He felt the Form was stretching and more, so he used the Form as part of the warm-ups for the advanced classes.

Q *How did he influence your T'ai-Chi – specific examples?*
A Master Liang very rarely just told us what to do without any explanation. He would always give us theory, principles and examples from the T'ai-Chi Classics.

One time I was given an old book on T'ai-Chi and I tried imitating the way the postures were done, which was an old style, quite different from the way Master Liang did the postures. Instead of telling me not to do them that way, he explained why he practiced the way he did and how the postures were modified and improved by the time he received them.

He usually presented his case with examples from the Classics, his many teachers and his own conclusions and then left us to choose for ourselves. From these kinds of experiences came a natural inquisitiveness and analysis that gave us personal freedom as students. Instead of becoming robots, we became researchers. Many times Master Liang said, "Followers are dead. Only rebels can get something." This taught us to learn, study and research from teachers, but in the end make it our own way.

Many times he pointed out that the different members of the Yang family each had their own way of practicing T'ai-Chi and that his teacher, Cheng Man-ch'ing, differed from his own teacher, Yang Cheng-fu. Master Liang taught us that the Classics' theories

Master Liang looking over the first edition of Lessons with Master T.T. Liang, *1994.*

and principles are constant and unchangeable, but what you did with them and how you executed them were personal.

Q What written sources do you know that feature or mention Master Liang?

A *T'ai Chi Ch'uan for Health and Self Defense* by Master T.T. Liang

    Drawing Silk: Masters' Secrets for Successful T'ai Chi Practice by Paul B. Gallagher

    Imagination Becomes Reality compiled by Stuart Olsen

    T'ai-Chi by Cheng Man-ch'ing and Robert W. Smith

    T'ai Chi Ch'uan: A Simplified Method of Calisthenics for Health and Self-Defense by Cheng Man-ch'ing

    Chinese Boxing: Masters and Methods by Robert W. Smith

    Martial Musings by Robert W. Smith

    Secrets of Shaolin Temple Boxing by Robert W. Smith

    Fundamentals of Tai Chi Ch'uan by Wen-shan Huang

    Tai Chi: The Supreme Ultimate by Lawrence Galante

    T'ai-Chi Ch'uan: Lessons with Master T.T. Liang by Ray Hayward

    The Way of Qigong: The Art and Science of Chinese Energy Healing by Kenneth S. Cohen

Q What would you want to ask him?
A At age 100, what is the happiest memory and why?

Q What is the one thing we should remember about Master Liang?
A His 10 Daily Theorems, because they are the essence of the T'ai-Chi Master Liang Tung-Tsai in his perfection. (Listed on pg. 12 of his book, *T'ai Chi Ch'uan for Health and Self Defense*.)

Additional Note:

Also, there are three songs which, whenever I hear them, immediately remind me of Master Liang. They are: "Old Man" by Neil Young, "To Sir with Love" by LuLu, and "Teacher" by Jethro Tull. Anytime I hear them, I am immediately transported back to my teens, soaking up the wisdom of the Master.

Master Liang and Jim Hayward, second son of the author, 1994.

Emperor T'ang's 100 Character Reminder

Translation & Commentary By Master T.T. Liang

The farmers work hard, but they themselves don't have much rice to eat.
Weaving girls work very hard, but they don't have much clothing to protect them from the cold.
You have three meals every day, the farmers have much bitterness.
You wear one thread of clothing, you have to remember the weaving girl's toil.
One inch of thread costs 1,000 lives (silk worms' lives).
One bowl of rice uses 100 whip lashes (on an ox's back).
You are not yet married, you still have some benefits,
But even sleeping and eating are not very comfortable.
You should make friends with the Virtuous,
It's best to quit a friendship without benefits.
Only take money entitled to you.
Don't take too much wine.
Restrain yourself from spending too much.
And, you have to shut your mouth.
If you can live according to my way, these 100 characters,
Your life will be truly successful.

Master T.T. Liang's Commentary

He lived quite long (Emperor T'ang).

He left 100 words or characters to remind you what you should do, what you should not do.

Shut up your bloody mouth, don't make friends with bad friends, get rid of wine, and don't dissipate.

Be a spendthrift, save money.

When you are wearing clothes you must think of the weaving girls; they torture themselves like hell, and the farmers work like hell. Then, as soon as you think of them, all right, don't dissipate, don't waste all these things.

What you should have, you take it. One cent not belonging to you, don't take it. That's all these things, so that you can follow his way. That means you'll be rich, become a high official, and keep good health for your whole life to last longer.

The following are free-form commentaries by Master Liang

T'ai-Chi Ch'uan Classic by Chang San-feng

In every movement, the entire body should be light and agile.
That means not use jerks. Relax.

And all of its parts connected like a string of pearls.
Connected together, no stops.

The ch'i should be stimulated.
This is the latent oxygen in your body, it's inside.

And the spirit of vitality should be retained internally.
Not let it go outside, reserve internally.

There should be neither deficiency nor excess, neither hollows nor projections, neither severance nor splice.
That means make it straight, don't incline, no stopping, no severance, don't cut it.

The energy is rooted in the feet, develops in the legs, is directed by the waist and moves up to the fingers. The feet, legs and waist must act as one so that when advancing and retreating, you will obtain a good opportunity and a superior position.
That means you are rooted on one foot, then developed to the legs and mastered by the waist, and afterward stretch out, spreading to the fingers. So, from the foot to the legs to the waist should be united as one unit. So, you step forward or backward, you get a chance and get an opportunity. So, you cannot get these two—what is chance and opportunity? Good opportunity means that you have the chance to find the defect position of your opponent. And in posture, that means you have your own superior position. You stand superior, they are not in a defect, this is no good. You must have these two, then you start to act. This is very important, when you are Pushing-Hands.

If you fail to gain these advantages, you will be in a state of disorder and confusion. The only way to correct this fault is by adjusting your waist and legs. The same principle applies to upward and downward, forward and backward, left and right. All the movements are to be directed by the consciousness within, rather than by the appearance without.

So, you cannot get a chance and good opportunity, which means that your body is all in confusion. Then how to adjust it? Up, down, left, right, you adjust, but use your mind. For everything, use your mind.

When attacking above, you must not forget below; when striking to the left, you must pay attention to the right; and when advancing, you must have regard for retreating. If an attack is proposed upward, the initial intent must be downward. If you want to pull something upward, you must first push downward, causing the root to be severed and the object to be immediately toppled.

That means you want to push upward, your intention go downward. If you want to pull something up, first, push downward, then the root will be severed. You push down, then go up. That means just like you pull up a tree or something, you have to go down and up.

Master Liang, also a master calligrapher, began painting at age 81.

The insubstantial and the substantial should be clearly discriminated. Each single part of the body has both a substantial and an insubstantial aspect at any given time and the body in its entirety has both an insubstantial and substantial aspect.

So this substantial and insubstantial must be clearly discriminated. Every place on the body has an insubstantial and substantial.

All the joints of the whole body are to be threaded together without the slightest severance.

The whole body should be connected together, no severance. What does this mean? If your weight is on the right foot, you push with the left hand and vice versa. If they push, you have to neutralize, not push back at the same time. These all must be clearly discriminated, not double-weighted. Then afterwards, we will explain Wang Chung-yueh's two Classics; they are very important.

Yang-Style T'ai-Chi Ch'uan Lineage

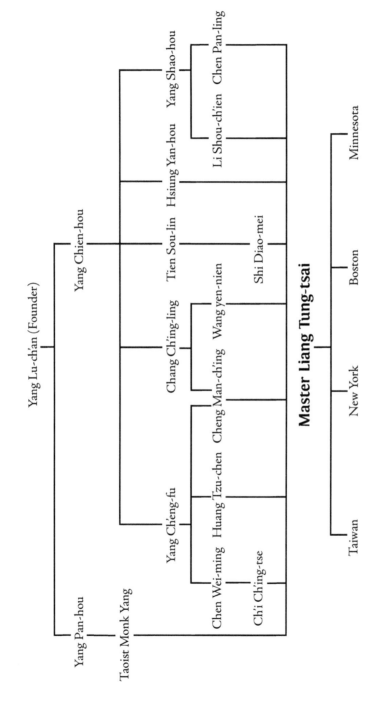

Yang Lu-chan (Founder)

Yang Pan-hou

Taoist Monk Yang

Yang Chien-hou

Yang Ch'eng-fu

Chen Wei-ming

Huang Tzu-chen

Cheng Man-ch'ing

Ch'i Ch'ing-tse

Chang Ch'ing-ling

Wang yen-nien

Tien Sou-lin

Hsiung Yan-hou

Yang Shao-hou

Shi Diao-mei

Li Shou-ch'ien

Chen Pan-ling

Master Liang Tung-tsai

Taiwan

New York

Boston

Minnesota

APPENDIX E

Wu-Dang Sword Lineage

Chang San-feng
(founder)

Chang Sung-hsi

Chao Ta-pin

Wang Chiu-cheng

Yen Hsih-hseng

Lu Hsih-niang (female)

Li Ta-nian

Ch'en Yin-ch'ang

Pi Yueh-hsia

Sung Wai-yi

Li Ch'ing-lin

Ch'i Ch'ing-tse

Liang Tung-Tsai

Shu-Kuang
(Ray Hayward)

Huei-Ming
(Paul Abdella)

Master T.T. Liang's translation of and commentary on the Man Chiang Hung Sword Form and the poem/song to which that form is practiced.

When you practice this Man Chiang Hung Sword, you have to know what it is. Suppose he says;

1. NO FAA CHUNG KUAN PING LAN CHU

My hair bristles in my helmet, I lean against the railing.

That means he is so angry, the hair on his head is standing up and making his helmet go up, come apart from his head.

2. HSAIO HSAIO YÜ SHIEH

The pattering rain has ceased.

The rain was pattering, but it stopped now.

3. TAI WANG YEN

I raise my eyes.

That means he is leaning against the rail; he's there thinking all these thoughts.

4. YANG TIEN CHANG SHIAO

And toward the sky I utter a long-drawn shout.

Then I raise my head; against the sky you have a long shout, WAAAAH! When you do it, you have to look up. Look to the sky.

5. CHUANG HUAI CHI LEH

My breast is filled with violence.

That means your mind is very, very disturbed—brave yet disturbed.

6. SAN SHIH KUNG MING CHEN YÜ TU
At the age of 30, fame and merits are but earth and dust.

Thirty years of special merit, he just became an official. What does it look like? Like dirt and earth, it's nothing. Because in this dynasty, in the palace, a very bad minister (Chin Kua) hates Yueh Fei, wants to kill him.

7. PA CHIEN LI LU YUN HO YUEH
Eight thousand miles of land are like the moon covered with clouds.

Eight thousand miles, you accompany the clouds and moon to Mongolia to fight. Chinese 8,000 equal 3,000 American miles.

8. MO TENG HSIEN PAI LIAO SHAO NIEN TO, KUNG PEI CHIEH
Do not tarry! The hair of youth grows white. Oh, vain sorrows.

That means you have to do something. Work hard; don't be lazy. Then your hair will become white very soon.

9. CHING KANG CHIE YOU WEI HSUEH
The shame of the year Ching-K'ang (1126) not yet wiped away.

That's means the emperor of this Song Dynasty, he's kidnapped by the Mongolian people. This is humiliating; you still didn't do anything. This emperor is kept in the Mongolian territory. So that's why he wants to fight.

10. CHEN TZU HEN HO SHIH NIEH
When will the hate of the subject come to an end?

That's why you stamp there. My hatred is strong. What time can I cancel this hatred?

11. CHIA CHIANG CHÜ TA PO HO LAN SHAN CHUEH
Oh, let us drive endless chariots through the Ho-lan pass.

So, I have to ride on a long carriage ride. I go to the mountain.

12. CHANG CHIH CHI TSAN HU LU JU (LO)
My fierce ambition is to feed upon the flesh of the Huns.

My very strong will, when I was hungry, I want to eat the Mongolians.

13. HSIAO TAN KO YIN SHUNG NU SHUEH

And, laughing, I thirst for the blood of the Barbarians.

Laughing, when I'm thirsty, I drink the blood of the Shung-Nu people.

14. TAI TSUNG TOU SHOU SHIH CHIU SHAN HO

Oh, let everything begin afresh. Let all the rivers and mountains be recovered.

When I come back, after I knock down the Mongolian people, I win the war. Then I come back to the beginning, to rearrange the emperor and country.

15. CHAO TIEN CHÜEH

Before we pay our respect once more to the emperor.

Then I want to see the emperor, kneel down, and say hello.

Then you have to do it, you have to act out with the sword, you have to know with the sword what you are doing. When it says to ride on the carriage, you walk around and around. This way, you have to act out according to what he says. If you don't know the meaning, and you do it, that means cast pearls before the swine, no use. Then when you know what it is, then you are doing exactly what he said.

Master Liang sitting in his basement in St. Cloud, Minn., circa 1986. He is in his pajama "uniform" that he often wore for classes at this time. The pants are tucked into his socks, which indicates that this photo was taken during class.

APPENDIX G

1987 interview, St Cloud, Minn.

Paul Abdella: Master Liang, could you tell us what the words T'ai-Chi Ch'uan mean?

Master T.T. Liang: T'ai-Chi Ch'uan is the classical dance for health and self-defense created about 700 years ago by a Taoist named Chang San-feng.

A: Could you tell us some general principles of this art?

L: What kind of principles you want to know?

A: Principles for health and self-defense.

L: Yes. First, this T'ai-Chi Ch'uan is for health. Let me explain why it's good for health. When you practice it, do not use externally muscular force. Not use the bones. Use internal muscles and sinews and tendons; the whole body goes as one unit. When you do it, it must be very, very soft. Then your blood will circulate through the whole body.

A: How about for self-defense?

L: For self-defense, gradually, after you practice, you will have a root. You will be firmly rooted. Then you have to learn Two-Person Dance, to know how to yield, how to neutralize, how to lose, not to gain. Gradually the body becomes so soft and flexible. That means to use only very little energy. To use four ounces to deflect the momentum of 1,000 pounds. That's the principle.

A: Are there different types or styles of T'ai-Chi, Master Liang?

L: Yes, quite a lot. I learned from, all together, fifteen teachers. Yang style, Wu style, Chen style, Hao style, these are a little bit different. But among them all, I prefer Yang style as the best.

A: How long have you been practicing Yang style?

L: Until now, at least, I think, 50 years.

A: Who was your teacher, Master Liang?

L: I had fifteen teachers, most of them are dead. The best of my teachers, I should say, is Cheng Man-ch'ing. He's dead already—when he was 74, something like that, now already more than thirteen years ago. He's the best because he knew all the Classics, can explain what the Classics are. If you want to learn T'ai-Chi, you must understand all the Classics. What did Chang San-feng put down? You have to follow his way with no mistake. Otherwise you cannot get it.

A: Master Liang, what are the T'ai-Chi Classics?

L: The Classics: one is written by Chang San-feng, another two are by Wang Chung-yueh.

A: These men were great masters of T'ai-Chi?

L: Of course, Chang San-feng is the founder, the creator of T'ai-Chi, and, after 200 or 300 years, Wang Chung-yueh adopted his way and explained more in detail about T'ai-Chi Ch'uan. These are the biggest masters of T'ai-Chi Ch'uan, these two.

A: It must be important, then, to become familiar with the Classics in order to perfect one's T'ai-Chi?

L: Of course, you must understand what it is. Then you do according to the Classics, then you will improve, then you'll achieve quite a lot. Otherwise you can never get it. So many teachers I had, only Cheng Man-ch'ing knew the Classics. The Classics were written in Chinese, using old-fashioned literature. The younger generation could not understand.

Master Wang Yen-nien, one of Master T.T. Liang's teachers, leading a class at Round Mountain in Taiwan in the 1970s.

A: Master Liang, I know that you practice calligraphy. How does calligraphy relate to T'ai-Chi?

L: Calligraphy is only a kind of hobby, where you sit down quietly and write. Don't put any energy, just relax your hand. The hand is soft and goes with the body. That means it should be quiet. It teaches you how to quiet down, be soft.

A: Just like T'ai-Chi?

L: Just like T'ai-Chi. Writing calligraphy is just like T'ai-Chi. In calligraphy, the words are both yin and yang. What time should it be harder, what time a little bit softer? This too, is hard and soft. The yin and yang should be coordinated, then you are writing at the highest level. Otherwise every word, every stroke is like dry branches. This is no good. Some hard and some soft, in coordination, then the character is good.

A: How does T'ai-Chi compare with other Martial Arts, such as Karate or Kung Fu?

L: Karate and these other arts mostly depend upon who is stronger to win. If you are very strong, you can knock someone down with one hit. Not use the whole body, just use muscular force. But T'ai-Chi is different. T'ai-Chi should be soft. Use your technique; use your art to conquer. This is quite different. The whole body goes as one unit. Gradually you have to learn that, then you get this art.

A: Have you ever practiced any of the other Martial Arts?

L: Of course. When I was young I didn't believe in T'ai-Chi. I learned many other kinds of Shao-Lin style—Praying Mantis and Shao-Lin Temple. In Shao-Lin Temple, there are many, many kinds of arts that, when I was young, I liked them. But when I was 45, I was sick in the hospital. When I got out, I could not do the hard ones, so I start to learn this soft one, from Cheng Man-ch'ing. Up to now I'm too old; I'm 87 years of age so I cannot do the hard ones. I don't want to do the hard way, the soft way is best for me. So that is why I have lived up until now.

A: So you believe that T'ai-Chi helped you regain your health when you were sick?

L: That's right. If I am sick and still not regained my strength, my body is still weak. If I do hard-style, it may hurt my heart and blood pressure, lots of trouble. Only by soft, very soft, moving very slowly, then your blood can circulate. So at first I learned T'ai-Chi just because it was interesting. Gradually it became a hobby, and then I became addicted to it. Then gradually you have to carry on, for your whole life. You cannot get rid of it.

Master T.T. Liang's 8-Step Praying Mantis teacher, Grandmaster Wei Shao-t'ang. This photo was taken in Taiwan in the mid-1970s.

A: Is it important to practice every day?

L: Of course. My teacher told me you'd rather skip one meal, not one round of T'ai-Chi. Very important, if you do two days and skip two days, that's no use.

A: Could you tell me, sir, what is the complete set of T'ai-Chi Ch'uan?

L: T'ai-Chi Ch'uan complete set would have the Form of 150 postures; left and right side. You do the right one and then the other side. Next you have T'ai-Chi Sword, right side and left side. Two-Person Form, both sides. T'ai-Chi Knife, with both hands and also Knife Fencing. After Knife Fencing, we have Double Sword and Double Knife, then you have T'ai-Chi Sword Fencing; you have Wu-Dang Sword Fencing and Staff Fencing—these all include both sides. When you learn all this, it is a complete one.

A: It sounds like it would take many, many years to master this entire art.

L: Of course, it took me more than 50 years. But if you are a genius, it takes you only three years! You can get the whole thing. It took me 50 years. But anyhow, even if you get the whole system or not, the chief purpose is you try to practice every day in order to keep good health. Self-defense is secondary. You want to live longer and enjoy life.

A: Who was the founder of the style you practice, Yang style, sir?

L: Yang Lu-ch'an. He learned from Chen Ch'ang-hsing in Chen Chia Kou. Yang Lu-ch'an was first generation and afterwards was Yang Pan-hou and Yang Chien-hou. And after was third generation Yang Shao-hou and Yang Cheng-fu. And after Yang Cheng-fu was Yang Shou-chung in mainland China. Gradually the form changed, was changed. Yang Lu-ch'an handed the form down to his sons; they changed it a little bit. Yang Cheng-fu is the best of all, very famous because he used the softest style, very soft.

A: Did Yang Lu-ch'an change the form from the Chen style?

L: Yes. He changed it quite a lot, to his own way. Mostly he taught T'ai-Chi Ch'uan formally, in Ching Dynasty; he only taught in the palace to the princes and the royal family. But after the Ching Dynasty fell, then come to the Republic of China, Yang's family came to teach to the outside. So outside, now everyone knows what is T'ai-Chi. Formerly no one knew what it was.

A: I understand that originally the Chen family would only teach to family members or people with the Chen family name. How was it that Yang Lu-ch'an came to learn this art from the Chen family?

L: According to the book, Yang Lu-ch'an was a hard-style martial artist. He heard that in Chen Chia Kou (Chen family village) that T'ai-Chi was good. He went to Honan (Henan) Province to Chen Ch'ang-hsing. He wanted to learn something from him but he knew that the Chen family won't teach outsiders, only their own family. So he pretended to be dumb, could not speak. Then he would sweep Chen's yard, if it was snowing or something. Every morning he would sweep the yard and try to find out. When he knew T'ai-Chi a little bit, but not much, one day he saw Chen Ch'ang-hsing with his students, all his family members, teaching in a room and the master was explaining, Yang Lu-ch'an peeked in from an outside window. Day after day he peeked and got a lot of things. Then one day Yang Lu-ch'an suddenly shouted because he got it, because he is so happy. Then they saw him peeking at the window. Maybe it was a bloody burglar! They caught him and pulled him down. "What the bloody hell you doing? You are the man who sweeps the floors, cleans the yard. Why are you bloody peeking

Master Liang with his classmate, Master William C.C. Chen in St. Cloud, Minn., 1985.

at the window?" Then he told them, "I am not dumb; I can speak, all right, and I want to learn from you, but you won't teach me. So I was secretly watching." Chen said, "This man is very good. He wants to learn something. Do you know something?" Yang said yes and practiced what he had learned secretly, and Chen saw he was really good and he would take him as his student. But before that he must try Pushing-Hands with his other students, Chen family students. Yang Lu-ch'an knocked them all down.

A: So he was quite gifted?

L: Yes, quite an expert. So Chen Ch'ang-hsing admired him and gradually showed him all his techniques. He got the art of Chen's family, Chen Ch'ang-hsing's whole art, the Chen style. Then one day Yang Lu-ch'an said he wanted to go back to Peking—he was a native of Peking—then they gave him a banquet. Chen told all his family members to come. Chen Ch'ang-hsing told all his family and students that he wanted to give all his family his art, but nobody got it. But this fellow, Yang Lu-ch'an, an outsider not belonging to our family, I don't want to it to give him, but he got it and now he's going to leave. Then Yang Lu-ch'an left. That's the whole story how he got the Chen family's art.

A: Are there any masters today, sir, whose art could compare to Yang Lu-ch'an's?

L: Nobody. The art has gone downhill since Yang Lu-ch'an. They say he had Sticking Energy. He had many kinds of energy according to the books. Even his sons could not acquire them all. They only knew very little.

A: Are there still some masters practicing today who have kept the art intact?

L: We don't know. So far as I know, in Red China, they have a Wu Style master named Wu Tu-nan. He is over 105 years old. And also the writer of the book, a Yang's family book, Yearning K. Chen, he is still in Red China. I think he is still living. He is over 80. So they have reached the highest standard.

A: And you yourself, sir, are 87.

L: Yes, sir, I am. I am nothing. I have got nothing, but I like it for my health.

A: If you are nothing that means you are everything, Lao Tzu's way.

L: Of course you have to yield. Don't be proud. Most of the masters say "I'm the number one, best of all," then trouble comes. Somebody will challenge you. The best way is to yield. Say "I'm nothing," no enemies, nobody challenge you. No enemies, all good friends. You have to yield, to give, not to gain.

A: These are principles of the Taoist, aren't they, sir?

L: Of course, T'ai-Chi Ch'uan is entirely based upon the Taoist way of Lao Tzu. Doing nothing, but nothing left undone. What does that mean? Everything done, it looks like nothing, yet nothing is left undone.

A: How often do you practice T'ai-Chi, sir?

L: Mostly three times a day and I teach quite a lot of students. About 40 minutes for one round of Solo Form, then Sword and weapons in the morning, in the afternoon at four o'clock and in the evening at seven or eight.

A: How was it that you came to the United States, Master Liang?

L: I came to the States because Cheng Man-ch'ing wanted to have an interpreter; he wanted to come here to show the public. Nobody could interpret for him, only I knew him quite well, so

Master Liang's 1963 passport photo.

he applied for me to come to the States. At first I did not like to come. I was retired from customs. I had some money and a house in Taiwan. I wanted to stay there for the rest of my life but Cheng Man-ch'ing insisted I had to go. I did not want to go. What for? America was new to me. I thought America was a barbarous country. If I came here, somebody may kill me. I could not understand their language. But Cheng Man-ch'ing insisted. He told my wife, "Let him go." My wife told me I better go. I said all right, before I go, I go to a fortuneteller. I said I want to know whether it is good or not that I go a far distance. He was a very famous fortuneteller in Taiwan; his name was Yuen Sho-shun. So I told him my birthday and age and where I was born, everything. He calculated and said it was very good to go, I could go. He said I had some enterprise to do in America. I said that I was retired and an old man, that I wanted to rest and do nothing. I was only going to go with Cheng Man-ch'ing for a little while and then come back. He said that all he could tell me was that I had something to do. So I went home and told my wife and then I went.

A: So when you came to the United States, Master Liang, with Master Cheng Man-ch'ing, you arrived in New York City? Is that correct?

L: Yes, my teacher was going to give a demonstration at the United Nations and I just interpreted, translated. Nobody else could do this work because all the Classics, from time to time, he had to mention them. Nobody could do it.

A: Because of your knowledge of T'ai-Chi you we able to make the accurate translations.

L: Yes. For many years I learned from him. He explained the T'ai-Chi Classics to me until I could understand it thoroughly. The T'ai-Chi Classics are very profound and abstruse theories. Suppose, according to the Classics, "You have hands all over your body but it has nothing to do with hands." What does this mean? Or, "When the lowest vertebrae are plumb erect, the spirit of vitality reaches to the top of the head. When the top of the head is as if suspended from above, the whole body feels light and nimble." What does it mean? These are the old Classics that I translated into English. Cheng Man-ch'ing always spoke from the Classics, but who could translate into English for him? In Taiwan, at the American Embassy Information Bureau, his relatives were working at that place. One day he gave a demonstration that I translated for him. Quite a lot of people were there. If he said something, I immediately translated for him. Then afterwards, his cousin or nephew, a young man at the embassy said why do we want to employ outsiders, this T.T. Liang, when we have our own staff? We can translate. He is Chinese; he thinks he can translate for Cheng Man-ch'ing. All right, one day Cheng Man-ch'ing gave a lecture and demonstration and he let his nephew translate. The result was that he couldn't do it because he didn't understand the Classics. Because, when Cheng Man-ch'ing spoke, then he had to stop there, the nephew can't translate, stop there. Everybody was laughing.

A: He did not know the Classics.

L: Right, he did not know the Classics. After that his nephew came to me and said, "T.T. Liang, next time you better come. I lose face. After one sentence I don't know it, I stop there." So next time, again, he had to request me to go. I went and had no trouble. Even if I made a mistake translating, I could make it up.

A: So how long did you teach or interpret for Cheng Man-ch'ing? Were you doing this for a long period of time or just for a short visit?

L: Not long. In Taiwan, just at the American Embassy several times, and in America, I teach

Master T.T. Liang lecturing at a college in New Hampshire in the early 1970s. He taught there for a year, then moved to Boston.

at the United Nations just one half-year. He only gave demonstrations there twice and also another one at Springfield College in Massachusetts, just one place. After that I taught there too.

A: How many years ago was it, sir, that you came to the United States?

L: I came here in 1963. It is now 1987. That means it is 24 years I stay here already.

A: Were there many people practicing T'ai-Chi in the United States?

L: At the beginning, when I came here, nobody knew what is this T'ai-Chi. Practicing in the park, people ask what are you doing, are you sick? They don't know. What is T'ai-Chi, Karate? I said, "No, it's T'ai-Chi." They don't know even the name. Since Cheng Man-ch'ing came here and I had been teaching somewhere, gradually, after a little bit, they know. And gradually, I don't know why, T'ai-Chi became more and more popular, not only here, but everywhere. That's an incredible thing.

A: So you and Professor Cheng could be given some credit for making T'ai-Chi popular in the United States?

L: Of course, yes. He is, from the point of view I came to, Cheng Man-ch'ing is the best. Including his art, not only T'ai-Chi art; his calligraphy; his painting and his poems. We call it Five Excellences. He plays chess. Oh, his chess is wonderful.

A: Chinese doctor as well?

L: Yes, Chinese medicine.

A: Where did you go to from New York City, sir? How long did you live and teach in New York?

L: About seven years. Terrible there, I don't like it, lots of trouble. I stayed in Ohio State University for some time. My son was there after he got his Ph.D. degree, then to New York and New Hampshire for about one-half year, then Boston for more than seven years. After that, I finally came to St. Cloud and Minnesota.

A: You came here to retire, Master Liang, I understand.

L: I want to retire because in St. Cloud I have my own house. I want to stay there, to hide up, to be a hermit, but I could not make it. Lots of people come to bug me and mug me. Not just from Minnesota, from different states, from foreign countries—including West Germany, England, Canada, Italy and France. So I want to stop, but could not. But anyhow, it is good for me to show and teach them so that I can take some exercise myself.

A: Had you been a T'ai-Chi teacher in China, sir, or in Taiwan?

L: In Mainland China I only have teachers; I learned from them. In Taiwan I had been a teacher for quite a long time. Because Cheng Man-ch'ing's students, of course he had a lot of students, I helped him teach. I learn from him and many others. He only knows the Short Form, 37 postures. After I learn from another man, he learned from Yang's family too—two of them, all from Yang's family—and put it into Long Form. I like the Long Form. I don't like the Short Form. Then afterward I learn from a man, this man is dead already, Hsiung Yang-hou, this Two-Person Dance. Then I learned Sword and Knife from different persons. Then I put all these things to the music. Cheng Man-ch'ing, my teacher, doesn't like it. He said, "You don't do this to music, spoil my game." I didn't care. I said Two-Person Dance must be with the beat.

A: Why do you practice T'ai-Chi to music, Master Liang?

L: In order to make it more scientific and more aesthetic. With music when doing it, no use to look at me, just listen to the music.

A: So you've introduced a kind of a rhythm?

L: Yes, rhythm. That's why, because you have to use rhythm to control yourself. Like meditation, you see. Like Dharuma, come to China, to teach the Buddhist way. When you meditate, sometimes you have to empty the mind, sometimes you have to use something

Mrs. Liang and daughter An Le.

to get rid of all outside thoughts. It's like Zen, when you do T'ai-Chi Ch'uan. When you meditate, you think, "what do I look like before I was born?" This question cannot be settled, never be settled. Gradually you will be peaceful and quiet, absolutely empty the mind.

A: So the beat or the rhythm of the music has a similar effect on the mind?

L: Yes. First you practice, one dah, two dah, three dah. You have to know where the beats are in the posture. Second, you have to not use the counts but use the beats in the music. Then after, forget the beats; only listen to the music. Then afterwards gradually the highest, forget the music but do just the same because you are accustomed to it. Naturally you will come to that way. No use to be thinking what is one, two, three and four. Forget it, but do it the same.

A: Master Liang, why should we practice weapons?

L: Because when you practice the Solo Form the energy only reaches to your hand, but when you practice weapons the energy can reach to the tip of this weapon. The energy goes further, longer.

A: You practice many weapons yourself, sir. Do you have a favorite?

L: My most favorite is Double Sword. I have Wu-Dang Sword, Ta-Mo Sword, also the two person T'ai-Chi Sword Fencing, I like. This is a favorite. I like most of them.

A: I see that you also have incorporated the use of the tassel on your sword forms. How did that come about, sir?

L: Because nobody knew how to use the tassel. One day I found one man named Li Chien-fei. He's still living in Taiwan. He showed me some forms and also he told me the use of the tassel.

A: What is it used for, sir?

L: The tassel is to induce you, to want to threaten you, then the sword comes. After this, he showed me some postures. Really the tassel is very useful. Sometimes the tassel comes down, then immediately the sword comes.

Mr. and Mrs. Liang outside their home in Taiwan.

A: So, to kind of confuse the opponent.

L: Secondly, he told me that in ancient times the tassel was not the kind made of thread, but of iron wire, very stiff, strong, may hurt your eyes. Frighten you first, then the sword comes. Immediately make you duck, then attack you with the sword.

A: At one time, then, the tassel was used as a weapon.

L: Yes, a weapon. He used the tassel to twist your sword, make you lose the sword, very effective. My teacher did it marvelously, so afterward I adopted the use of the tassel with weapons. A lot of people don't know it. But after I learned from him, I adapted it to all my way—Double Sword, Double Knife, Two-Person Fencing, everything using the Sword and Knife, how to use the tassel.

A: When should a person begin to practice Pushing-Hands?

L: After learning the Solo Form, then you have to learn Pushing-Hands. Learn the Solo Form, then you will have a root. Just stand there and nobody can push you over. You have to do it the correct way. Then gradually, learn how to counter the attack. When somebody cannot push you, then to push him or her you have to use technique. So you have to learn Two-Person Dance.

A: What does it mean to have a root?

L: When you have a root, you can stand there and nobody can push you over. You gradually practice every day. Just like a tree, you have a root into the ground 3 or 4 feet deep. You presume you have a root that goes down. You practice the correct way, not let the knee pass over the toe. That's floating, that's no good. Gradually you practice and then automatically you are firmly rooted.

A: So like the roots of a tree, a little bit every day, your roots will go deeper?

L: Yes, deeper and deeper but you must do it the correct way. Follow all the Classics. You practice that way, then you will have a root. Otherwise you can never get it.

A: T'ai-Chi is also called a soft or internal form of Martial Arts. What does that mean?

L: It is internal, not external. External uses the bones. Internal uses the whole body as one unit. When you push, don't just use the hand, use muscle, tendon, sinews, then go very soft. When you go out, not hard-style, but use the whole body as one unit. Don't let the ch'i go up; ch'i should sink to the tan-t'ien. It's quite strong. In the beginning you don't get it, but after, you'll get it, really. Like Cheng Man-ch'ing, at the beginning, with just a little move of his hands, he knocked me down; I went 8 feet away and fell down.

Paul Abdella and Diane Cannon visiting Master Liang at his retirement home in New Jersey. Liang was in his late 90s.

A: I've read in your book, sir, that you've developed Ten Theorems for daily life. Could you tell us some of those?

L: These are things I have learned since teaching in the United States. Lots of trouble. Lots of students come to bug me and mug me. Even opponents come to bug me and mug me. Terrible things happened. When I first came to the States, I had retired from customs. I had reached the highest rank of customs officer, like an admiral. When I come to the States, I despised everybody. I thought I was the number one. Gradually I faced a lot of trouble. Somebody come to bug you and mug you, you get trouble. Then I think I

Master Liang's 8-Step Praying Mantis teacher, Grand Master Wei Shao-tang.

have to give up this, try to yield, try to lose, try to be humble. Not to be angry. Then I formulate these ten guiding principles. Anything come to me I follow these ten guiding principles to act. Even the police come to find trouble with me, to my studio. Lots and lots of trouble.

A: Did your practice of T'ai-Chi help you to develop those Ten Theorems?

L: Yes. Gradually you know how to yield. Don't be angry; don't make enemies. Just like my ten guiding principles. The first says, so when you read books, don't entirely believe it. If you believe in books entirely, better not to have books. Books sometimes are wrong. Teachers are the same thing. You learn from them what is good. If they have bad things, get rid of it. Don't expect that everything from a teacher is good. Sometimes his art is good, his character is no good. Don't learn from his character, only learn from his art. If you believe in teachers entirely, better not to have teachers.

)What is wait? To wait is painful. I wait a long time to finish this interview....

Articles about Master T.T. Liang from Twin Cities T'ai-Chi Ch'uan Studio Wu Dang Newsletter by Ray Hayward

Wu-Dang, Vol 1, No 2, September 1993
A Story about Master T.T. Liang

While studying with Master Liang in Boston in the late 70s, one of his favorite quotes was number 56 in the *Tao Te Ching*: "Those who know do not talk. Those who talk do not know." He would use this to keep "experts" in line. To further our confusion, Master Liang would quote the first part of a poem by Po Chu-i, which goes something like this:

(If) Those who know do not speak,
And those who speak do not know,
Then how could Lao-Tse write a book of 5,000 characters?

We debated this among ourselves without coming to any conclusion. Did Lao-Tse know or not? Finally we approached Master Liang. We asked him that if those who know do not speak and that if the *Tao Te Ching* was full of truth, how could Lao-Tse write a book of 5,000 characters?

Master Liang answered, "Somebody had to."

Wu-Dang, Vol 2, No 1, January 1994
94-Year-Old Grand Master T.T. Liang Visits the Twin Cities T'ai-Chi Ch'uan Studio

"Beautiful! Their postures are quite correct and their movements are exactly on the beat." So spoke Master Liang after 28 members of the Studio performed the Solo Form on Nov. 16. Looking everybody up and down, Master Liang checked everyone's postures as he "reviewed the troops." The huge, beaming smile he broke into after the final bow radiated acceptance and approval.

A farewell demonstration for Master T.T. Liang in St. Paul, Minn., on October 23, 1988.

Master Liang then answered questions about the early days of learning T'ai-Chi, from extreme sickness, to gradual recovery, then realizing good health. He told of studying with Professor Cheng Man-ch'ing and coming to America to translate for him while teaching at the United Nations in 1963. We heard some explanations on how and why T'ai-Chi is good for health. He also told of the days living under imperial rule in China, and of the early days of the Republic, even about following a then-young Chou En-lei to a protest of a corrupt governor.

"I want to see some Pushing-Hands!" Master Liang suddenly barked. The students then demonstrated some Pushing-Hands drills and the Four-Directions. He made a few corrections and then, with Joanne Von Blon as his partner, gave some tips from the T'ai-Chi Classics. *"In Ward-Off, Roll-Back, Press and Push, one must know the correct technique.* This means that you must distinguish and execute the four hand movements correctly. *Use a push and pull of four ounces to deflect a momentum of 1,000 pounds.* This means that when you use Roll-Back, you use four ounces of energy to turn your body to neutralize a 1,000-pound-force push. *Entice them to advance; when their energy is emptied, adhere to them and issue energy.* Induce them to come to you. Then when you neutralize them and they're in a defect position, you push them over. No. You must closely connect to them, then push. Then your push will be effective. In Chinese we say, *Ho Chi Ch'u,* which means to get close to them, adhere to them, then you issue energy."

We ended the night with the members lining up to shake hands with Master Liang, who took an on-the-spot survey of how many "boys and girls" were present. Master Liang was then surprised when Kim presented him with the customary red envelope of appreciation. Obviously deeply moved, he thanked the students for their kindness and hospitality.

All in all, it was an evening filled with fun, excitement, stories, teasing (at Paul's expense) and a deep sense of connection to the master and advisor of our Studio, Master T.T. Liang. Thanks to him and to all who came (even two old-timers, Bob Geis and Bob Klanderud) and made it a great time.

Wu-Dang, Vol 5 No 4, May 1997
Meeting Master Lin Chun-Fu

On May 12-14, I had the pleasure of meeting and studying privately with Master Lin Chun-fu at his home in Irvine, California. Master Lin and his son Paul, welcomed me, opened their home and offered their time to me. Master Lin is a classmate, student, and was a practice partner of Master Liang's from when they were in Taiwan. Here is a short list of his teachers and the arts he learned from each:

Master Shang Tung-sheng – Chinese Wrestling
Master Wei Shao-tang – 8 Step Praying Mantis
Master Wang Shu-jin – Hsing-Yi and Pa-Kua
Master Chi Ching-tse – Wu Tang Sword
Master Li Chien-fei – Shaolin Weapons
Master Han Chin-tang – Chin-Na
Master Liu Pei-jung – Taoist Meditation
Master T.T. Liang – T'ai-Chi

Here are some teaching points I received through private instruction and conversations with Master Lin.

"Pa-Kua is the circle walk."

"Use Pa-Kua's twisting actions to escape joint locks."

"When you practice the circle walk, relax and be empty inside so you can get filled with ch'i."

"The hands and arms must follow the body, never the body following the hands."

"Once I developed my hands as weapons, anything I put in my hands can become a weapon."

Ray Hayward with Lin Chun-fu one of Master Liang's training partners.

"When you practice Chin-Na you open the opponent's joint, then you close it again, but in the wrong place."

"Chinese wrestling lets the opponent come in and follows their movement. When they change, that is the opportunity to counterattack. Judo takes the throw, but Chinese wrestling lets you give them the throw."

"You are very lucky. You have a good teacher. Mr. Liang learned from great masters, reached a high level himself and is willing to teach what he knows. He also encourages you to study from many different teachers. In my generation, this was rare among the masters."

Wu-Dang, Vol 8 No 4, June 2001
Principles not Postures

Master T.T. Liang was famous not only in Taiwan but also in North America for his skill and knowledge of T'ai-Chi Ch'uan. We were always amazed at how many times we would go to class only to find a visiting teacher or practitioner talking with Master Liang and asking for advice, guidance and corrections.

Many times we saw Master Liang ask the visitor to show him some of their form. (I always noticed that the higher-level practitioners did a section or a part of a form,

In his late 90s, Master Liang let his mustache and goatee grow out.

while the lower levels "treated" us to their entire form.) Master Liang would then give corrections, advice from the Classics, practice suggestions and encouragement to the many who came from all over the United States and Canada.

Many of Professor Cheng Man-ch'ing's students came up from New York City asking for instruction and anonymity. We saw many practitioners of Wu, Chen and many variations on the Yang style T'ai-Chi—as well as Shao-Lin, Praying Mantis and others—scrutinized by the master and then sent on their way, happy, refreshed and with new insights into their arts.

One time I asked Master Liang how he could give corrections to all those different styles and methods. Most of them didn't do the form like us, or even our style, yet they knocked on the door seeking instruction. Master Liang answered, "Because I correct their principles, not their postures."

Wu-Dang, Vol 10, No 1, October 2002

End of an Era

August 19, 2002, ended an era that began on January 23, 1900, and encompassed the most amazing changes in the world and in one person. Our teacher, Master T.T. Liang, passed away peacefully after a brief battle with pneumonia. He was 102. Master Liang rallied two days before passing, during which time he gave his attending nurses a lecture on T'ai-Chi from his book.

Master Liang's impact on the T'ai-Chi world, and to many of us in our personal worlds, is immeasurable. Invited by the United Nations to assist his master, Professor Cheng Man-ch'ing, in introducing the art of T'ai-Chi Ch'uan to America, Master Liang taught an estimated 3,000 students from 1965-1995. Master Liang practiced what he preached when he said, "T'ai-Chi is the whole world exercise." His book on T'ai-Chi is the best for non-Chinese speakers.

A Buddhist memorial service was held at our studio on August 28, 2002. Close to 100 people attended, including Master Liang's daughter, An-le Wang. At the end, 65 people got up to do one round of the Solo Form to the music with Master Liang counting—a fitting conclusion.

PAGE B6 • STAR TRIBUNE ★ TUES., AUG., 27 • 2002

Obituaries

Master of t'ai-chi, T.T. Liang, 102, dies

A native of China, the renowned martial-arts teacher lived 10 years in Minnesota.

By Nolan Zavoral
Star Tribune Staff Writer

T.T. Liang, who taught the ancient martial art of t'ai-chi ch'uan to thousands of Americans, including several hundred Minnesotans, died last week at 102 in Andover, N.J.

Liang, who spent a total of 10 years in St. Cloud during two stays, will be remembered at a memorial service today at 6 p.m. at the Twin Cities T'ai-Chi Ch'uan Studio, 2242 University Av., St. Paul. Liang's daughter, Anle Wang, will attend, said the studio's co-owner, Paul Abdella, who studied with Liang.

Liang (pronounced lay-AHN) was venerated as a master of the millenniums-old discipline that combines mental and physical elements. Developed by Chinese monks to defend themselves against attacks by bandits and warlords, t'ai-chi ch'uan has been taught as a meditative outlet as well as a self-defense measure.

"Master Liang taught that there were four main elements to t'ai-chi ch'uan," Abdella said. "There was health, self-defense, mental development and meditation. And, he said, health came first."

Liang credited his own longevity to the t'ai-chi ch'uan, former students said. When he was 45 and suffering from liver problems because of a loose lifestyle, Liang happened upon the discipline.

In his popular 1977 book, "T'ai-Chi Ch'uan," which is still in print, Liang wrote, "I must keep on practicing for my whole life; it is the only way to preserve health."

Liang, from northern China, emigrated to the United States in 1963, along with his renowned teacher, Cheng Man-Ching. For nearly two decades, Liang taught t'ai-chi ch'uan in Boston and New York at such prestigious schools as Tufts and MIT.

He moved to St. Cloud in 1981 — at the age of 81 — to live near his daughter and son-in-law, and retire. However, his reputation preceded him, and he resumed a busy teaching schedule.

"A whole bunch of us scampered up there [from the Twin Cities]," Abdella said. "We begged him to take us as his students."

In Liang, Abdella said, the Twin Citians found "the classic profile" of a t'ai-chi teacher — "he was the wise old sage, a Yoda, and very humorous."

Liang left St. Cloud in 1989, to live in Tampa and Los Angeles with relatives, but returned in 1995. By that time, his wife had died, and he required assisted-living.

He left Minnesota for good in 1997, settling in New Jersey.

— Nolan Zavoral is at nzavoral@startribune.com

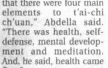

T.T. Liang told his students that he credited his long life to the discipline of t'ai chi ch'uan.

Master Liang's obituary from the Minneapolis Star Tribune.

Wu-Dang, Vol 10, Nos 2-3, June 2003
Going to Northfield

The last year of his life,
102 of them and then some,
Saw winter, spring and summer,
But not fall.
So I will witness this autumn,
Let him borrow my earthly senses,
And enjoy it all the more for the both of us.
Have the geese flown so high,
Were the leaves ever this colorful,
Did fall smell so good,
This past century?
Is this the first time
The world is on the brink of war,
Leadership is riddled with corruption,
Or the old ways die a slow death?
I think not.
And it is not the first autumn
That a student sat thinking
How much they missed their teacher.

Wu-Dang, Vol 11, No 2, January 2004
Some Reminiscences on Fifteen Years of Discipleship

From Webster's Dictionary
disciple – *a pupil, follower or adherent of any teacher or school of religion, learning, art, etc.*
lineage – *1. descent in a line from an ancestor, 2. ancestry, family*

November 11, 2003, marked the 15th anniversary of my discipleship ceremony in which I became a formal student of Master T.T Liang and a lineage holder of Yang style T'ai-Chi Ch'uan. I'd like to share some of my experiences.

In Boston, Master Liang gave us six months' notice to finish whatever we were working on because he was "retiring" and moving to Minnesota. I knew most of Master Liang's system, and I could learn the few remaining forms from my classmates, but there was something I desperately wanted—discipleship.

I can't tell you how many times Master Liang would be talking about someone and he would make a distinction by saying the person was a "disciple" or a "formal student," or he would say the person was "only a student." I asked him what the difference was between a disciple and a student? He told me that the old masters would only teach the highest levels, the secrets, to their disciples and family members. He also said only a disciple formally inherited the system.

One difference between the Chinese and Westerners is that the Chinese value the lineage over the individual. They don't care how advanced you are; they judge the sum total of the master and teachers of a particular school. In the West, we tend to value the individual and his accomplishments. Master Liang cautioned us many times to "never forget your roots; don't forget your ancestors who passed this art on to you."

At the end of a class night, Master Liang would pack up his things and leave us to practice and lock up while he went across the street to his apartment. I always carried his bag and belongings and walked him the half-block home, waiting while he unlocked the front door to his building. One night I couldn't take it any longer and I blurted out, "Master Liang, please take me as your disciple!" He looked at me for a moment, then said quietly, "No." I asked him, "Is there more I need to learn? Is there anything I can do to prove my sincerity?"

"No, it's not that," he said. "You have to understand, I don't take disciples because I want all my students to be equal with me. In the master-disciple relationship, the master is the boss, the superior. I did that in the Customs Service." Being a foolish, impatient young man I didn't really listen to him. "What about all the secrets? I need to learn them," I said. "I taught that all freely," he said. I left, dejected.

Seven years later, a similar scene transpired. Master Liang told us that he had put his home in St. Cloud up for sale and was moving to Tampa to retire. Because we believed

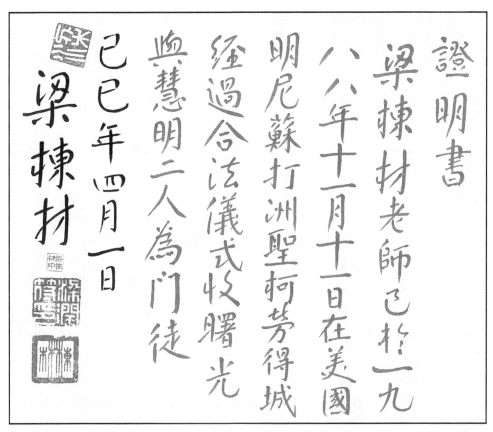

The disciple certificate written in Chinese by Master T.T. Liang for Ray Hayward (Shu-kuang) and Paul Abdella (Huei-ming) on November 11, 1988, in St. Cloud, Minn.

him this time, the Studio organized a farewell demonstration for Master Liang. I, my classmates and an assortment of students put on a two-and-a-half-hour demo showing Master Liang his complete system, including Praying Mantis and Ch'in-Na. At the conclusion of the demo we were told that Master Liang's house had been sold and that he would be moving in a month!

At this time, Paul Abdella and I were the last students who regularly drove to St. Cloud for a weekly private class. My friday-night time slot was the last class Master Liang would be teaching, seeing as he was packing and flying out the next week. Paul and I made the one-hour drive, and the class started as all the others had, with the Solo Form. This time though, instead of watching and correcting, Master Liang got up and did the round with us. We then went on to do a few more forms, and then Liang asked, "What's next?" I said, "Sir, we want to be your disciples." He said, "No. No need." I said, "Really, sir, that's what we want." Master Liang answered, "All right" and proceeded to go upstairs to the kitchen.

We packed up our stuff and went upstairs. Master Liang said, "You must have a witness." He called one of his daughter's friends, Amy Roske, who lived a few blocks away, to come over. Amy stood to the side as Master Liang sat in a chair to receive our Kow Tow (*kow*-9, *tow*-head). Nine times Paul and I prostrated ourselves before Master Liang, our heads touching the floor in front of him. The first six bows Master Liang accepted, during the last three he returned the bows. "You must pay the witness," Master Liang said. I tried to give Amy some money, but she said she didn't do anything to deserve it. I ended up hiding the money in her coat. It was done.

A few days later I called Master Liang in St. Cloud and said, "How are you, sir?" He answered, "How should you address me now that you're my disciple?" I said, "I don't know what's proper." He said, "You should call me Shih-fu, but it's all right if you still call me sir."

Three months later Paul and I were in Tampa visiting Master Liang at his new home. His son Joseph met us and told us that his father was happy he had made us disciples. "My father is proud of you two," Joseph told us. At the end of a great visit, Master Liang said to us, "You two are the only ones I ever gave a (discipleship) calligraphy to. I never expected to have disciples. I am happy I gave these to you two—a good choice."

So what about the secrets? Master Liang had taught all the secrets in the regular classes. In the old days, you became a disciple, then you received the "good stuff." In my experience, I received the good stuff, then I became a disciple.

Thank you, sir.

Wu-Dang, Vol 11, No 3, June 2004
Green Comes From Blue:
Further Reflections on Discipleship

Master Liang went into semi-retirement in 1990 and fully retired in 1995 at the age of 95. His teaching career spanned 30 years, from 1965-1995. In the United States, as well as Taiwan, it is estimated that he taught more than 3,000 students. That is a lot of Single-Whips! Master Liang's teaching can be summed up in two phrases: "T'ai-Chi is for everybody, a whole-world exercise" and "I want my students to be better than me." It is the latter that I want to address.

One time after a class, Master Liang told us about a phrase in Chinese, "Eight characters that sum up my philosophy about teaching." He recited it in Chinese and then gave a quick translation. "Green comes from blue, green excels the blue." He went on to tell us that green is considered a "higher" color than blue because it has yellow in it. (Yellow was the sacred color of the emperor, known as the Son of Heaven.) But green also has blue in it. He said the basic meaning is "to be better than your teacher." He said his sincere wish is that all his students become better than he, that they reach a higher level and teach more people, and that they improve the art to be more accessible to the masses.

Master Liang and his wife celebrating his 83rd birthday in St. Cloud, Minn.

After Master Liang told us about "Green Comes from Blue," I asked him to make me a calligraphy of that saying in Chinese. He said, "I will when your T'ai-Chi is better than mine, when you have learned more than I have, taught more students than I have, wrote more books and articles about T'ai-Chi than I have, and you have four children who are Ph.D.s!"

In 1988, I was pretty much finished with Master Liang's curriculum, putting the finishing touches on Double Sword and Wu-Tang Fencing. I was both elated and sad—the end of a phase of learning, which started in 1977, was coming to a conclusion. It was at this off-balance "Na-position" that he gave me the last counterattack I was to receive from him. "If only a few got it, my art is no good. I want to pass on an art that is accessible for everyone."

At this point I made two plans—short term and long term. The short-term plan was to organize a demonstration of Master Liang's complete curriculum and show him all the facets of his teaching. In October 1988, the Studio gave a three-hour demonstration to an audience with Master Liang front and center. His whole teaching career was laid out before him, from the Solo Form to partner-work, to numerous weapons. The majority of demonstrators were my classmates (Liang's students) and students of Liang's students. The demo was filmed and subsequently made into a DVD and is available to the public. To say it was beautiful is an understatement. Master Liang got into the spirit of the event and performed T'ai-Chi San-Shou and Double Sword with Tassels.

Master Liang was extremely happy and proud. We showed him that not only did his art pass to many of his direct students but also to many of the next generation as well. There were no doubts about his impact in the T'ai-Chi world and his continuing lineage. Mission No. 1 completed—now the hard part.

My long-term plan is to change my focus from trying to be the best practitioner of T'ai-Chi (Master Liang always said, "Don't try to become Yang Lu-ch'an," i.e. the highest level), to becoming the best promoter of the art; to shift from collecting to distributing; to pass on an art truly user-friendly to

Master Liang, who earned an MA, had children who were Ph.D.s. Paul Gallagher gave Liang the title, "Ph.D. of the Ph.D.s!"

everyone regardless of race, sex, health, age or anything; and to help students save their precious time by helping them avoid pitfalls, while still getting the experience of the pitfalls.

A lot has happened since 1988.

I have one personal disciple who passed through the traditional disciple ceremony. Since 1994, Paul Abdella and I bestowed a modified ritual of initiating students as disciples of the lineage. Many of these disciples made good on their discipleship and used the extra recognition and responsibility to take their T'ai-Chi to the next levels.

I received by mail a formal request for personal discipleship, using the traditional ceremony of initiation. This got me thinking about tradition and change. I am now considering this student and am thinking of changing back to the old way of taking personal disciples after they show a certain level of proficiency and dedication and after receiving a formal request for discipleship from them (those who have already received discipleship can opt to have the experience by renewal through the traditional ceremony). I do this not to promote or aggrandize myself, but to insure the respect, dedication and commitment to T'ai-Chi that a lineage-holder should maintain.

Lao-Tse says in the *Tao Te Ching* that "ritual is the beginning of ignorance." The classic commentaries on this verse clarify it by pointing out that Lao-Tse was talking about ritual with no knowledge, or meaning, behind it. As I grow older, I see what needs to be updated and modified in the art of T'ai-Chi Ch'uan. I also see what needs to be kept and preserved. I feel that the ritual of discipleship deserves to be brought into the 21st century. The teacher/student or master/disciple relationship is the best way to ensure the transmission of any art.

As I write this, I am reminded of the excitement and responsibility of being a disciple of Master Liang.

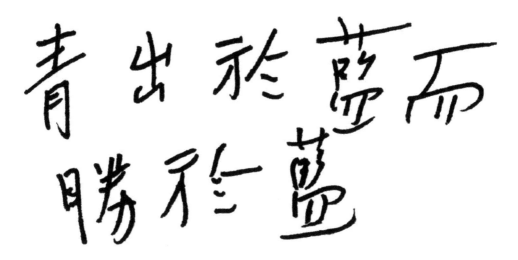

This is Master Liang's own calligraphy and translation:

Ching	Chu	Yue	Lan
Er	Sheng	Yue	Lan
Ching Green	Chu Comes Out	Yue From	Lan Blue
Er But	Sheng Exceeds, Excels, or Surpasses	Yue From	Lan Blue

Green comes from blue,
Green excels the blue.

Wu-Dang, Vol 13, No 3, June 2006
Remember Silently

I would like to quote a line from the T'ai-Chi Classics and explain some of its concepts. In the T'ai-Chi Ch'uan Treatise by Wang Chung-yueh, there is a line that says: *After you have learned to interpret energy, the more you practice, the better your skill will be, and by examining thoroughly and remembering silently, you will gradually reach a stage of total reliance on the mind.* I will relate an experience that happened to me more than 25 years ago pertaining to the part about examining thoroughly and remembering silently.

When I was first learning T'ai-Chi, I became friends and a practice partner with one of Master Liang's senior students. We practiced together and shared everything and it was a very good relationship. At one point, I was able to move into a private class offered by Master Liang, which my senior classmate could not attend because it was a closed class and he worked nights. I would meet with Master Liang on Friday nights in the private class, and then get together and practice with my senior classmate on Saturday mornings before the group Solo Form class. One day, Master Liang saw me teaching my senior classmate the lesson of the previous night. Master Liang took me aside and said, "Don't teach him that; it's for you right now."

The following week, no sooner had my private class begun than Master Liang criticized me and asked how I could be teaching someone else a lesson or concept I had just learned myself and had no time to digest, understand or perfect. He said to me, "The Classics, The Classics, you must remember The Classics. The Classics say: *Examine thoroughly and remember silently.* Examine thoroughly means that you must understand the lesson from your teacher and practice hard so you can get it. Remember silently means that until you understand exactly what it is, you should not tell anyone or teach anyone what you are working on."

The next day my senior classmate asked me what I learned in my private class the night before. In a very untactful and disrespectful way, I said, "I can't tell you." He pressed me for a better answer and I said, "Well, actually, I learned that I can't share my lessons with you anymore." Seeing him become angry, I explained the line from The Classics and told him that Master Liang had expressly forbidden me from teaching anything that I hadn't been practicing, or understood, for a long time. My classmate became very angry and confronted Master Liang, who then fired back at my friend, saying he should take private lessons of his own if he wanted to learn.

The next week I got together with my senior classmate to practice as usual, but the damage had already been done. We began practicing Pushing-Hands, and it quickly escalated into a very aggressive and competitive situation. We stopped practicing the T'ai-Chi way and practiced like two bulls fighting. We ended that practice session, our last, in silence and enmity, with him having been injured. We were never to be friends again. If I could go back in time, that situation would not have ended that way. My conclusion

Master T.T. Liang was the head of customs in Taiwan. Liang, in his Customs Service uniform, holding his daughter, An Le.

was far from Master Liang's teachings and T'ai-Chi's philosophy.

Sometimes from a very bad experience, you can learn a very good lesson. This particular line in The Classics has become a rule and guide for me. *Examining thoroughly* has been a lesson about my relationship to myself and whatever particular lesson I am working on. *Remembering silently* is about my relationship with my practice partner. How can I teach something that I just learned myself and have not had time to explore or catalog or digest? I have also learned a facet of human nature—if I tell my partner a particular thing I'm working on, it seems that that is the one thing that is avoided and won't get worked on. For me, *examining thoroughly* also sums up the learning philosophy of one of my other teachers, Master Wai-lun Choi. Master Choi, at different times in my lessons, either encouraged me to "go to research" or to "go to analyze." For Master Choi, the word "analyze" means going to a teacher, learning the lesson, figuring out what it is that you are going to practice, "making sense of what you are going to practice," and then taking it home and practicing. "Research" means all the study, insight, discovery and skill that you will get from your practice and "practicing to find out what you will get from your practice." I made a mistake for many years by considering them the same. I have gone back and researched all my notes, and I now have a deeper meaning of his teachings.

At our studio, we are fortunate that there are many senior students now who are able to give good instruction. It is also in such an open atmosphere that students feel free to ask questions of other students. I would not discourage this. I would suggest that if your teacher were standing right next to you, it would be more appropriate for you to ask the teacher your question than the person you're practicing with, who may or may not really understand what you're doing. Be careful that you get good, solid answers to your questions. Time is precious, and The Classics are very clear in telling us that *if you do not seek carefully in the direction indicated, your time and effort will be spent in vain, and you will have cause to sigh with regret* and *a slight error or deviation results in wide divergence from the true way. Therefore, the student cannot but thoroughly discriminate the right and wrong. For this reason, The Classics have been made.* In the Classic called "Song of the Substance and Function of the 13 Postures," one line tells us to *examine and investigate carefully and thoroughly.* I hope you examine thoroughly and remember silently this article.

Wu-Dang, Vol 14, No 3, June 2007
Opening Our Altar

T'ai-Chi Ch'uan as a martial art does not have an external showing of rank or accomplishment, like the more common colored belts of other styles. One way to assess an individual's progress and ability is by their knowledge of the system, which consists of theories, principles, history, philosophy and the various forms and practices.

Another ranking system consists of time spent practicing and is called small success, medium success and big success. Some masters consider the small success (or small accomplishment) as having completed five years of continuous practice, focusing on the external parts of the art. The medium success is considered having completed seven years of continuous practice, merging the internal with the external parts of the art. The big success constitutes completing ten years of continuous practice, balancing the internal and external aspects of the art. Some masters feel that counting years of practice is not as accurate because unless you regularly practice, one year might only yield a few hours of practice.

Another way of looking at the three successes is delineating the small success as having completed 100 hours of practice, the medium success as 1,000 hours of practice, and the big success as 10,000 hours of practice. Master T.T. Liang, in his book *T'ai Chi Ch'uan for Health and Self-Defense* (pg. 75), gave this milepost, "It is my opinion that when one has mastered the techniques of Roll-Back and Receiving Energy, one has acquired the art of T'ai-Chi and reached the highest level."

There's also another system of rank and progress that is highly ritualistic and borrows heavily from Chinese culture and a mixture of Buddhism, Confucianism and Taoism. The system is based upon relationship and time. When someone is first studying, one is a student. One's responsibility is to oneself and to learning the art correctly. After studying for a considerable time and learning a good portion of the system, a student is then asked to help out and give back some experience, understanding and ability to the studio. This may be as simple as performing small tasks or tutoring new students. This person can be considered a senior student, which has nothing to do with their age or the time they have been attending the school.

When someone has extensive experience and has spent a great amount of time, both in personal practice and tutoring, this person is considered an instructor or teacher. This person will be given a class or classes to teach under the supervision of the master.

When a practitioner feels so moved by a particular style or teacher and they want to officially join with that lineage, they then apply for discipleship. When they have passed through a solemn ceremony, that person is considered a disciple. A disciple is just like being part of the master's family.

Whenever Paul Abdella and I meet with or talk to Master Liang's children, Joseph Liang in Florida and An-le Wang in California, they call us "brother" and accept us as part of their family. Some teachers call their disciples their "inner door students." This refers to an old-fashioned Chinese house where guests and visitors were allowed into the courtyard and common rooms, "the outer door," while only family and special guests were allowed in the private living spaces of the house, "the inner door." This shows closeness and trust.

Although being a disciple and lineage holder is a senior rank, there is yet a deeper connection with the master and lineage. This is called "opening the altar." The altar is a place of reverence and respect. It is common in the Chinese household to have an altar to pay respect to one's parents or family, or to worship and adore particular gods, goddesses and deities. It is an honor and sign of acknowledgment, permission, recognition and connection for the master to come and offer incense and devotions at the altar of his student's school. This "opens" the altar, which allows the virtue of the lineage to flow into the school, and the respect and appreciation of the school to flow back to the ancestors. Master Liang always admonished us to "never forget your roots; you must pay respect to the ancient masters who passed this art on to us."

We opened the doors to our current studio on September 14, 1993. In October 1993, Master T.T. Liang came to our studio and officially opened our

Master Liang at age 98.

Master T.T. Liang opening the altar at Twin Cities T'ai Chi Ch'uan Studio, 1993.

altar. This private ceremony was witnessed by a handful of students and was followed by a celebratory meal at a local restaurant. The above photos show our altar and Master Liang lighting incense and offering his devotions. When the incense burned down, I took the three sticks that were left and have kept them as a memento of what I consider my highest privilege as a disciple.

If you have passed a formal ceremony and have become a disciple and lineage-holder, there is still one more rank and honor to be awarded to you: to have your own altar opened.

Appendix I

From Twin Cities T'ai-Chi Ch'uan Studio's Chinese New Year Demonstration Program February 3, 2007

Some Reminiscences of 30 Years of Practicing T'ai-Chi Ch'uan

By Ray Hayward

"Thirty years is a short time when exploring the mysteries and enjoying the benefits of the art of T'ai-Chi Ch'uan." -Shu-Kuang

This year marks my 30-year anniversary of learning and practicing T'ai-Chi. Although my exact date is July 31, 2007, I am taking this year to look back on 30 years, to celebrate and share, and to project and dream about another 30 years.

I began my T'ai-Chi journey in 1977 after practicing Kenpo Karate for four years. I had been reading many books about martial arts, and T'ai-Chi interested me. I began looking around for a T'ai-Chi instructor and first began practicing a style called Hwa Yu T'ai-Chi. I had read that a famous T'ai-Chi teacher, Master T.T. Liang, was teaching in Boston, but he did not advertise, and I couldn't find his school or him. At the Hwa Yu School, the instructor

Master Liang's 100th birthday party, January 23, 2000, in Andover, New Jersey.

lent me one of T.T. Liang's books that included photographs of him. While walking down the street one day, I actually recognized Master Liang passing on the sidewalk. I stopped him and asked if I could study with him. He told me to come the following week, and that began my great good fortune.

I learned the complete system of Yang Style T'ai-Chi Ch'uan from Master Liang as well as Praying Mantis, Ch'in-Na and various weapons. Not only did I study at various studios in Boston but I practiced in two parks with Master Liang: the Rose Garden at Fenway Park and the Public Gardens next to the Boston Common. I also followed Master Liang to Minnesota, and I visited and studied with him in Florida, New Jersey and California. I met many classmates and friends while studying with Master Liang, most notably my three Pauls: Paul Parrotta, Paul Gallagher and Paul Abdella.

I also learned Yang style T'ai-Chi and studied the T'ai-Chi Classics with Paul Gallagher. I learned Chen style T'ai-Chi with Dr. Leung Kay-chi, and, for the past few years I have been learning the combined style of T'ai-Chi from Grand Master Wai-lun Choi. Here is an example of how differently two masters can look at the same principle: Master Liang told us to tuck our hips but to be careful not to tuck too much. Master Choi on the other hand stressed that you can't tuck your hips enough.

Teaching has been an integral part of my journey. First as a helper in Master Liang's classes, then by being given my first teaching assignment by Master Liang, and eventually teaching around the Boston area, I got a lot of teaching experience. I was a guest instructor at the first five Deer Mountain Taoist Academy retreats in Vermont. I've taught T'ai-Chi in Massachusetts, Vermont, Delaware, Pennsylvania, Virginia, Michigan, Florida, New York, and Winnipeg, as well as many places in Minnesota. And I even taught a short course in London.

I am truly lucky. I found the art that I wanted to practice for my whole life at an early age. I am just as excited to learn and practice today as I was 30 years ago. I am still researching and exploring daily, and I am eager to share my findings. I am seeking to refine my art and to continue my journey towards the unseen and mysterious. I've spent the past 30 years learning, practicing and researching the entire system, as well as exploring other systems. I had heard from many sources that T'ai-Chi as a system was missing parts and that the self-defense and higher levels of meditation had been lost. Master Liang always told us, "Everything is in it [T'ai-Chi]—all the practical use and Taoist meditation." Because Master Liang's emphasis had been on health and well-being, the self-defense and fighting aspects were not emphasized. Although Master Liang knew them, and taught us many of the advanced theories, techniques and principles, he was most concerned with health and the "changing of temperament." After studying with Grand Master Wai-lun Choi, I was able to see that T'ai-Chi is indeed a complete system and has all the components and levels. Through Master Choi's guidance, I was able to see the training methods necessary to bring these out.

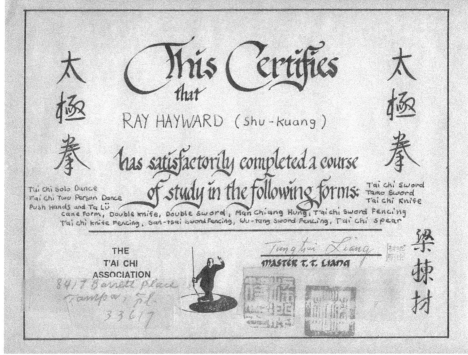

Two versions of a certificate that Ray Hayward received from Master Liang to commemorate his completion of Liang's complete curriculum.

What do the next 30 years hold for me? If I'm granted 30 more years of life and health, then the following are some of my foreseeable plans and goals. I want to refine the right side of my Solo Form, while strengthening the left side. I want to practice the complete T'ai-Chi Ch'uan system every day. I have a few changes to make to the Solo Form and some for the weapons forms and San-Shou as well. I would like to catalog the complete system in books and DVDs, and I have a third of my next project, a book about the Pushing-Hands, already written. I would like to fine-tune and make the most out of the Studio's schedule, open a second studio and find two apprentices to train as my successors. Thirty years from now I will be 77, the same age Master Liang was when I met him. He was just beginning the most productive and influential stage of his T'ai-Chi teaching career. I hope by then to be seeing my students reaching the peak of *their* teaching careers.

When I began studying T'ai-Chi, Master T.T. Liang was 77 years old and had just reached his 30th anniversary of T'ai-Chi practice. Many times he would begin a lesson with: "After 30 years I found this to be true or that to be true." I can now say that after 30 years I have some truths, or rather, experiences, I would like to share with you.

1. Concerning the Solo Form, I believe it is good in the beginning to practice it in a group, with a leader or an outside rhythm and tempo. After 30 years I believe the only way to master your Solo Form is to practice it by yourself with your own internal rhythm and personal speed.

Master Liang at his Los Angeles home in 1993.

2. With all my teaching experience, I believe that female students should begin practicing the Pushing-Hands exercises with other women for the first six months so that they become empowered and comfortable before they join a mixed gender class. I believe men need to emphasize sensitivity when first learning the Pushing-Hands exercises and strive to proportionally increase their skill while decreasing their aggression.

3. After 30 years of reading, studying, researching and practicing the principles and theories from the T'ai-Chi Classics I can now say that some of the Classics are wrong, some I fully understand, some I know even better than the writer, some I haven't deciphered and some are still truly profound and mysterious.

4. I've had some really great teachers. How do I define a great teacher? They must possess four essential qualities: They have to be able to get me to the next level, they have to be able to teach me how to learn, they have to show me a new way of looking at old material and they have to inspire me, not necessarily with their skills, but with their knowledge, commitment and enthusiasm. A good teacher is someone who knows how to put the right carrot in front of the right donkey.

5. I look at students as tortoises and hares. I'm not impressed with quick results. I am more impressed with longevity, commitment, loyalty and perseverance. Master Liang warned us that when you practice T'ai-Chi, "even ten years is a short time."

6. Paul Gallagher coined the phrase "Tai-Chi friends." Those are the people you work out with, not against. You share a common bond of research and practice. Paul Gallagher taught me the scholarly and gentlemanly way to compare skills and understanding. I was more than happy when I was younger to compare my skills, full out and full ego. This, of course, makes many enemies. To work slowly with another person, looking at techniques in great detail, is the fast track to accomplishment. I try to instill this method in my classes so that everyone will have a good partner and be a good partner. Indeed, one of the sayings that we use at the Studio came from this experience. Maybe you've heard someone say, "A good partner is worth 1,000 gold bars."

7. Did I mention sacrifice? In any pursuit there must be sacrifice, compromise and loss. On this night of celebration I don't feel it is appropriate to tell the tale of my own personal sacrifices, compromises, and losses.

8. I would say that group classes are great, but I don't believe I could be where I am now without continuous private classes. From the very beginning, I studied

Ray Hayward and son Alex visiting Master Liang's basement studio in St. Cloud, Minn., 1988.

with Master Liang in weekly private classes, as well as in group classes. The vast majority of classes I've studied with Master Choi have been private lessons. I don't believe you can learn deeply if your only exposure to T'ai-Chi is through weekend workshops and seminars. There is magic in T'ai-Chi. I can't define that magic but I've experienced it many times and it has always been person to person. In a good teacher-student relationship, the mystical and unspoken lessons are conveyed through that relationship. The Chinese call this "passed from my mouth to your heart." It's hard for this to happen in a crowd, although occasionally, it does.

Next year I celebrate 30 years of practicing Praying Mantis Kung Fu, and the following year, Hsing-Yi and Pa-Kua. I would like to conclude with one thought and one summation.

Here's my thought:

If speed, power, youth, aggression and arrogance are the secrets of T'ai-Chi, then it is no better than any other exercise or martial art. What makes T'ai-Chi the "supreme ultimate" is slow-motion, softness, yielding, non-action and humility. I believe these are the real secrets. They are not hidden, or lost, but are out in the open for anyone brave enough to embrace them.

After 30 years I feel I can use four words to sum up my T'ai-Chi experience so far:

relax

sink

unify

enjoy

About the Author

Sifu Ray Hayward (Shu-Kuang) began his health maintenance and Martial Arts training in 1973, studying Kenpo Karate and Jiu-Jitsu. In 1977, he met and began study with Master T.T. Liang in Boston. Ray learned the complete Yang Style T'ai-Chi Ch'uan system from Master Liang, as well as Praying Mantis, Ch'i-Kung, Taoist Meditation, Ch'in-Na, Wu Dang Sword and various weapons. In 1984, Ray moved to Minnesota to continue studying with Master Liang. In 1988, Sifu Hayward passed through a formal ceremony to become an inner-door disciple of Master T.T. Liang.

Ray studied Northern Shao-Lin Long Fist, Praying Mantis, Pa-Kua Chang, Hsing-Yi Ch'uan, Chen Style T'ai-Chi Ch'uan, Ch'in-Na, and various weapons with Dr. Leung Kay-chi. He studied Northern 7-Star Praying Mantis and Fanzi Eagle Claw with the late Sifu Lo Man-biu.

Ray learned Taoist Meditation, Qigong, 5 Animal Frolics, and T'ai-Chi Ruler from Masters Paul B. Gallagher and Kenneth S. Cohen.

Other teachers include Master William C.C. Chen, Master B.P. Chan, Mr. Heinz Rottmann, Mr. Li Wang, and Sensei John Duncan.

Sifu Hayward rounded out his martial arts education by studying with Liu Ho Ba Fa Grandmaster Wai-lun Choi, learning Hsing-Yi Ch'uan, Pa-Kua Chang, Y'i-Ch'uan, Qigong, Taoist Meditation, and Wu Dang Sword.

Ray privately studied Kwong Sai Jook Lum Southern Praying Mantis, Sin-Kung and Calligraphy with Grandmaster Gin-foon Mark.

Ray currently studies Luk Hop Bat Fat with Grandmaster Wai-Lun Choi, and Modern Tactical Martial Arts with Master Rob Jones. He studies the breath technique and methods of Wim Hof and Stig Severinsen.

With a deep interest in spirituality and meditation, Ray has explored many Eastern religions, focusing on Taoism and Sufism. Ray studied 11 years with Sufi Master, Shaykh Nazim al Haqqanni an Naqshbandi. He has also studied Hypnotherapy, Psychology, and is certified in the Healing Tao System. He has made extensive research and study concerning the Western Mysteries, including Alchemy, Freemasonry, the Knights Templar, Rune Lore, the Rosicrucians, Druidry, Celtic history, and Rosslyn Chapel, studying with such masters as David Sinclair Bouschor, Joseph Lang, Charles W. Nelson, Timothy W. Hogan, and Philip & Stephanie Carr-Gomm. In 2010, Ray became a Druid Graduate in the Order of Bards, Ovates and Druids.

In 1979, Ray began teaching T'ai-Chi as an assistant under Master T.T. Liang in Boston, and then as a full-time instructor in Minnesota from 1984 to the present. From 1984 to 2016, he was the chief instructor for the Twin Cities T'ai-Chi Ch'uan Studio. Ray has taught T'ai-Chi at the Sister Kenny Pain Clinic at Abbott Northwestern Hospital, Hazelden Treatment Center, Courage Center, General Mills World Headquarters, Virginia Piper Cancer Center, Minneapolis Public Schools, the Northfield Community Education Department, and Carelton College P.E. and Rec Department. He has also conducted seminars, workshops, and retreats throughout the United States. Internationally, Ray has taught in Winnipeg, Canada, and in London, England.

Sifu Ray Hayward has taught martial arts to hundreds of people, particularly T'ai-Chi Ch'uan, as a way to gain health, peace of mind, physical confidence, and a state of well-being. His goal is to empower, not overpower, others.

"Forty years is a short time when exploring the mysteries and experiencing the benefits of the art of T'ai-Chi Ch'uan."

-Ray Hayward

Master Liang's calligraphy of the author's Chinese name, Shu-Kuang, which means "first ray of the morning light," or "hopeful conditions."

Contact Information

Mindful Motion Tai-Chi Academy
www.mindfulmotiontaichi.com
Facebook: facebook.com/Mindful-Motion-Tai-Chi-Academy

Ray Hayward Enterprises
www.rayhayward.com
skrayhayward@gmail.com

Grandmaster Wai-lun Choi
www.liuhopafa.com

Paul Gallagher
www.totaltaichi.com

Kenneth Cohen
www.qigonghealing.com

Gin-foon Mark
www.masterginfoonmark.com

Dr. Leung Kay-Chi
www.jiannshyongkungfu.com

Order of Bards, Ovates and Druids
www.druidry.org

Timothy W. Hogan
www.lulu.com/spotlight/Emerys

Sensei Rob Jones
rrpj72@gmail.com